Theme Skills Tests
Table of Contents

Author's Introduction T3

Features at a Glance T4

Using the Theme Skills Tests

Purpose and Description ..T5

Administering the Theme Skills Tests T6

Using Test Results to Plan for Instruction T7

Houghton Mifflin Reading: A Legacy of Literacy Resources for Meeting Individual Needs T8

Theme Skills Tests

Practice Test 1

Theme 1: Nature's Fury 3
  A. Sequence of Events 4
  B. Text Organization 6
  C. Categorize and Classify 8
  D. Information and Study Skills ...10
  E. Base Words 12
  F. Syllabication 13
  G. Word Roots: *struct* and *rupt* 14
  H. Spelling 15
  I. Vocabulary 17
  J. Grammar 19
  K. Writing Skills 21

Theme 2: Give It All You've Got 23
  A. Fact and Opinion 24
  B. Story Structure 26
  C. Predicting Outcomes 28
  D. Topic, Main Idea, and Supporting Details 30
  E. Information and Study Skills ...32
  F. Compound Words 33
  G. Roots *spec/t* and *opt* 34
  H. Suffixes *-ward* and *-ous* 35
  I. Suffixes *-ive* and *-ic* 36
  J. Spelling 37
  K. Vocabulary 39
  L. Grammar 41
  M. Writing Skills 43

Theme 3: Voices of the Revolution 45
  A. Author's Viewpoint 46
  B. Cause and Effect 48
  C. Following Directions 50
  D. Information and Study Skills ...52
  E. Possessives and Contractions 54
  F. Syllabication: VCCV and VCV Patterns 55
  G. Prefixes *sub-* and *sur-* 56
  H. Spelling 57
  I. Vocabulary 59
  J. Grammar 61
  K. Writing Skills 63

Theme 4: Person to Person . . .65
  A. Problem Solving and
    Decision Making 66
  B. Noting Details 68
  C. Compare and Contrast 70
  D. Making Inferences 72
  E. Information and Study Skills . . .74
  F. Syllabication: VCCCV Pattern . .76
  G. Syllabication: VV Pattern 77
  H. Words Ending in *-ed* or *-ing* 78
  I. Suffixes *-ly, -ness, -ment,*
    -ful, -less 79
  J. Spelling 80
  K. Vocabulary 82
  L. Grammar 84
  M. Writing Skills 86

Theme 5: One Land,
Many Trails 89
  A. Drawing Conclusions 90
  B. Propaganda 92
  C. Making Judgments 94
  D. Story Structure 96
  E. Information and Study Skills . . .98
  F. Prefixes *un-, dis-, in-, re-;*
    Suffix *-ion* 100
  G. Stressed and Unstressed
    Syllables 101
  H. Syllabication 102
  I. Changing Final *y* to *i* 103
  J. Spelling 104
  K. Vocabulary 106
  L. Grammar 108
  M. Writing Skills 110

Theme 6: Animal
Encounters 113
  A. Making Generalizations 114
  B. Topic, Main Idea, and
    Supporting Details 116
  C. Drawing Conclusions 118
  D. Information and Study Skills . .120
  E. Prefixes *com-, con-, en-, ex-,*
    pre-, pro- 122
  F. Three-Syllable Words 123
  G. Suffixes *-ent, -ant, -able, -ible* . .124
  H. Spelling 125
  I. Vocabulary 127
  J. Grammar 129
  K. Writing Skills 131

AUTHOR'S INTRODUCTION

Dear Educator:

Teachers have always used a variety of assessment strategies to help them evaluate student progress and to make instructional decisions. Taken together, these strategies can form a coherent assessment system.

A good assessment system has three essential elements. First, it includes a variety of informal and formal assessments. Second, it helps teachers integrate assessment during instruction and use that information to adjust their teaching. Finally, a good assessment system includes both teacher and student self-assessment throughout the learning process.

Houghton Mifflin Reading: A Legacy of Literacy provides teachers with assessment options to fill all these needs. In this program you will find Integrated Theme Tests, Theme Skills Tests, Benchmark Progress Tests, and the new Leveled Reading Passages.

Houghton Mifflin Reading: A Legacy of Literacy also provides extensive support for assessment integrated into the instructional plan in the *Teacher's Edition* that accompanies the anthology. There you will find informal diagnostic checks and suggestions for reteaching, student self-assessments, comprehension and fluency checks, and test-taking strategies. Other strategies are in the *Teacher's Assessment Handbook*.

Not all teachers, students, or school districts need the same assessment system. By reviewing the various options in *Houghton Mifflin Reading: A Legacy of Literacy*, you can determine which pieces best meet your needs. Enjoy the many opportunities assessment provides to get to know your students and to help them grow.

Sheila Valencia

FEATURES AT A GLANCE

Theme Skills Tests

✔ Are criterion referenced.

✔ Test specific skills taught in the theme.

✔ Include comprehension, information and study skills, structural analysis, vocabulary, spelling, grammar, and writing skills.

✔ Can be administered before the theme (pretest) or following the theme.

✔ Have individual skill subtests that can be administered separately.

✔ Have a multiple-choice format with a single correct answer.

✔ Are in consumable and blackline-master format.

USING THE THEME SKILLS TESTS

PURPOSE AND DESCRIPTION

Purpose

The Theme Skills Tests assess students' understanding of discrete reading and language skills taught in each theme of *Houghton Mifflin Reading: A Legacy of Literacy.* The Theme Skills Tests are designed to help you evaluate students' understanding of these skills and use the results of the evaluation to customize future instruction to meet the needs of your class and of individual students. The tests may also be useful as preparation for certain standardized assessments.

Description

The Theme Skills Tests are made up of subtests covering comprehension, information and study skills, structural analysis, spelling, vocabulary, grammar, and writing skills. The comprehension and structural analysis sections are divided into subtests for each of the individual skills taught in the theme. Each subtest includes five or ten multiple-choice questions.

- **Comprehension Skills:** Each comprehension subtest includes a passage followed by multiple-choice questions that cover key concepts in the text. The test items evaluate students' ability to comprehend the reading and apply the skills to the passage.

- **Information and Study Skills:** This subtest is designed to assess students' ability to apply the information and study skills taught in the theme. The skills might include one of several special methods of gathering information, such as reading a map, chart, or graph, or using the dictionary.

- **Structural Analysis:** Each subtest is designed to assess students' ability to apply new phonics and decoding strategies. A test item might consist of a sentence to complete or one with an underlined word or phrase to explain or reword.

- **Spelling:** The spelling subtest assesses students' ability to recognize the correct spelling of words they have studied in the theme. Students read ten sentences, each containing a blank. They must choose the word that is spelled correctly.

- **Vocabulary:** The vocabulary subtest consists of ten items. It assesses students' ability to apply new vocabulary skills. A test item might require students to identify a word that is a member of a particular word family or use a provided dictionary entry to determine the part of speech.

- **Grammar:** The grammar subtest consists of ten items. It checks students' understanding of the grammar skills taught in the theme.

- **Writing Skills:** The writing skills subtest assesses students' understanding of the writing skills taught in the theme. Students are given five questions in a multiple-choice format.

ADMINISTERING THE THEME SKILLS TESTS

You can schedule the use of the test in any of several ways:

- After completing a theme, you can administer the entire Theme Skills Test or selected subtests to help determine how well students understand the skills taught in the theme.

- You can administer selected subtests at the beginning of the program or at the beginning of a theme to diagnose students' strengths and weaknesses. You can use these results to plan the appropriate level of instruction.

- You can administer any part of the test during the course of the year in order to evaluate areas where students may need additional help.

When you administer one or more parts of the test, follow these guidelines:

- Distribute the test or subtests to be given. Check during the test to make sure students are completing the correct portions of the test.

- Check to make sure students understand how to take the test and how to mark their answers. You may wish to administer or review the Practice Test. For the Practice Test, have students read and follow the directions. Then discuss the correct answer with them. You may also want to discuss any questions students have regarding how to mark their answers.

- During the test, allow students to work independently, but help them with any directions they do not understand.

- Allow students sufficient time to complete the subtests. Use as many sessions as you feel are necessary to accommodate students' needs.

USING TEST RESULTS TO PLAN FOR INSTRUCTION

Scoring: Using the Skills Test Record Form

Because the Theme Skills Tests are a simple multiple-choice evaluation, scoring is direct and objective. Correct answers are shown on the annotated pages of the *Teacher's Edition.*

In general, a score of 80 percent on any section of the test should be accepted as an indication of satisfactory performance. Thus, if a student scores 80 percent or above, you may assume his or her understanding of a skill is adequate.

Tips for Planning Instruction

If a student demonstrates mastery of a skill application by scoring 90 percent or above, consider using the challenge suggestions throughout the *Teacher's Edition* and in the *Challenge Handbook.*

If a student answers fewer than four out of five questions correctly, he or she may need more help with the particular skill. It is important, however, to consider other evidence of a student's growth in reading (from other assessment instruments and your own observations) before concluding that the student is not performing satisfactorily. For example, you may want to review your notes on the observation checklist or the student's work on *Practice Book* pages for the skill. Monitor the student's work on similar skills in the next theme's instruction for an overall view of his or her progress. Check the Skill Finder in the *Teacher's Edition* for the next occurrence of the skill in the level. You may wish to give special attention to the student in teaching this next lesson.

If a student performs very poorly on the Theme Skills Tests, or seems to not benefit from extra support, she or he may need intervention support. The need for intervention can be assessed using various diagnostic measures, which are outlined for you in the *Teacher's Assessment Handbook.*

For information on how to best accommodate English language learners, consult the *Language Development Resources* book.

HOUGHTON MIFFLIN READING: A LEGACY OF LITERACY
RESOURCES FOR MEETING INDIVIDUAL NEEDS

If results from the Theme Skills Tests determine that a student needs challenge or extra support in a certain skill area, consider modifying instruction using the following resources.

	Extra Support	**Challenge**
Comprehension	• *Teacher's Edition*, Throughout each selection: Extra Support and Previewing the Text boxes; Supporting Comprehension questions; Wrapping Up questions; Review/Maintain Lessons • *Teacher's Edition*, Theme Resources: Reteaching Lessons for Comprehension Skills • Blackline Masters: Reader's Library; Selection Summary • Other Reading: Theme Paperbacks (easy), Classroom Bookshelf (easy)	• *Teacher's Edition*, Throughout each selection: Challenge boxes and Reading Cards; Responding questions and activities • *Teacher's Edition*, Theme Resources: Challenge/Extension Activities for Comprehension • Other Reading: Theme Paperbacks (challenge), Classroom Bookshelf (challenge)
Structural Analysis	• *Teacher's Edition*, Back to School: Phonics/Decoding Lesson in the Strategy Workshop • *Teacher's Edition*, Theme Resources: Reteaching Lessons for Structural Analysis Skills • Intermediate Intervention • CD-ROM: Lexia Quick Phonics Assessment	• CD-ROM: Wacky Web Tales

RESOURCES FOR MEETING INDIVIDUAL NEEDS (continued)

	Extra Support	Challenge
Spelling	• Basic Words • Extra Support box	• Challenge Words • Challenge box
Vocabulary	• *Teacher's Edition*, Extra Support box: Vocabulary Support	• *Teacher's Edition*, Vocabulary Skills: Expanding Your Vocabulary • Theme Resources: Challenge/Extension Activities for Vocabulary
Grammar	• *Teacher's Edition*, Theme Resources: Reteaching Lessons for Grammar Skills	• CD-ROM: Wacky Web Tales
Writing Skills	• *Teacher's Edition*, Reading-Writing Workshop: Student Writing Sample; Tips for Getting Started; Tips for Organizing; Improving Your Writing; Student Self-Assessment • Writing Skills: Improving Your Writing	• *Teacher's Edition*, Reading-Writing Workshop: Reading as a Writer; Publishing and Evaluating • Theme Resources: Writing Activities • Journal Writing • Revisiting the Text: Genre Lessons; Writer's Craft Lessons

If a student has overall poor test scores but does not seem to be struggling in class, check whether time allotment, directions, or test format may be contributing factors. You may review the Preparing for Testing section in the Theme Assessment Wrap-Up. Also consider the level of support a student is receiving in class. An independent task such as this test may disclose that the student is experiencing more difficulty than may have been apparent. You may want to check in the *Teacher's Assessment Handbook* for other assessment options to help you analyze the student's understanding of the tested skills.

Overall poor performance on tests and in class may indicate that the assigned work is too difficult for the student. In this instance, you may wish to have the student use the Reader's Library during the next theme.

For more extra support and challenge ideas, consult the *Extra Support Handbook* and the *Challenge Handbook,* as well as the *Education Place* Web site.

Name _____

Practice Test

Read the paragraph. Then read the question and fill in the circle next to the best answer.

Bessie Coleman, who was born in 1893, loved to fly airplanes. Yet she could not get into a flight school in the United States. In those days, the schools did not admit people who were African-American. Coleman found a school in France that would accept her. Later, she became the first African-American to earn a pilot's license. When she returned home, Coleman discovered that the airlines would not hire her as a commercial pilot. However, Coleman did not give up her dream. She learned how to do stunt flying, or barnstorming. People who visited air shows loved to watch her perform. During her life, Coleman also worked to help African-Americans and women who shared her dream.

Read the following question. Fill in the circle next to the best answer.

1. Which sentence best describes what this paragraph is about?
   - ● **A.** Bessie Coleman overcame many challenges to become a pilot.
   - ○ **B.** Bessie Coleman became a well-known barnstormer.
   - ○ **C.** Bessie Coleman was the first African-American to earn a pilot's license.
   - ○ **D.** Bessie Coleman went to flight school in France.

Nature's Fury

Level 5, Theme 1
Theme Skills Test Record

Student _____ Date _____

Student Record Form		Possible Score	Criterion Score	Student Score
Part A:	Sequence of Events	5	4	
Part B:	Text Organization	5	4	
Part C:	Categorize and Classify	5	4	
Part D:	Information and Study Skills	5	4	
Part E:	Base Words	5	4	
Part F:	Syllabication	5	4	
Part G:	Word Roots: *struct* and *rupt*	5	4	
Part H:	Spelling	10	8	
Part I:	Vocabulary	10	8	
Part J:	Grammar	10	8	
Part K:	Writing Skills	5	4	
TOTAL		70	56	
	Total Student Score x 1.43 =			%

Sequence of Events

Read the passage. Then read each question and fill in the circle next to the best answer.

What a Blast!

On a spring morning in 1980, an earthquake shook the ground under Mount St. Helens in Washington. As a result, one side of the mountain slid away.

The earthquake created the largest landslide ever. It also awakened a volcano that had been quiet for over one hundred years. Just after the earthquake occurred, a blast of hot gas, steam, and rock spewed into the air. A huge cloud of ash rose fifteen miles into the sky. The ash was then picked up by the wind and scattered over 22,000 square miles.

Over 150 square miles of forest were flattened by the blast. A scorching fire following the blast burned the forest to the ground. When the fire died down, scientists went in to view the area. They saw that the beautiful mountain scene now looked like the surface of the moon.

A few months after the eruption, new plants began to appear in the blast zone. After several more years, the plants had spread across the area. Later, a few tiny trees sprang up from cracks in rocks. Following the trees, coyotes, foxes, and elk began to return to the mountain.

Today the volcano is a laboratory for scientists, who have made many discoveries. For example, they have learned how an ecosystem can renew itself and about the power of volcanoes.

1. What happened just before the landslide at Mount St. Helens?
   - ○ **A.** Ashes were scattered over 22,000 square miles.
   - ○ **B.** Coyotes, foxes, and elk came to the mountain.
   - ○ **C.** The forest was burned by a scorching fire.
   - ● **D.** An earthquake happened under the mountain.

2. Which event happened first?
   - ● **F.** A blast flattened over 150 square miles of forest.
   - ○ **G.** Scientists viewed the area destroyed by the volcano.
   - ○ **H.** A fire burned 150 square miles of forest.
   - ○ **J.** A few tiny trees sprang up from cracks in rocks.

3. When did the events in the fourth paragraph take place?
   - ○ **A.** before the eruption
   - ○ **B.** during the eruption
   - ● **C.** in the years following the eruption
   - ○ **D.** one hundred years after the eruption

4. Which of these shows the order in which living things returned to the mountain?
   - ○ **F.** animals, plants, trees
   - ● **G.** plants, trees, animals
   - ○ **H.** trees, animals, plants
   - ○ **J.** plants, animals, trees

5. Which signal word or words from the last paragraph show a time shift from the past to the present?
   - ● **A.** Today
   - ○ **B.** discoveries
   - ○ **C.** For example
   - ○ **D.** renew

Name _____

Text Organization

Read the passage. Then read each question and fill in the circle next to the best answer.

Spotting a Tornado

A small funnel-shaped cloud dropped from the slowly moving storm. As it grew larger, the cloud twisted violently like an angry snake. Two miles away, the people in the small town of Water Valley, Ohio, watched in horror.

The people of Water Valley had reason to be frightened. Small funnel clouds can quickly turn into fierce tornadoes that touch the ground. The wind speeds in a tornado may reach 200 to 300 miles per hour. Such powerful tornadoes can destroy everything in their path.

Tornadoes are carried along by the storm clouds in which they form. They may move in a straight path or appear to skip from place to place. This irregular movement makes it difficult to guess where tornadoes will move next — and it makes them more dangerous.

Look at the pictures below. If you ever see such a sight, take cover.

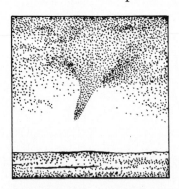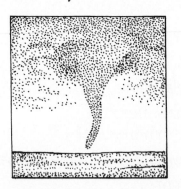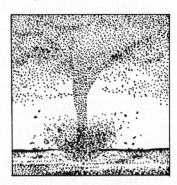

A tornado first appears as a small funnel-shaped cloud dropping out of storm clouds.

Go on ⟹

1. How is the passage organized?
    ○ **A.** by listing the events in the Water Valley, Ohio, tornado
    ○ **B.** by explaining what to do if you see a tornado
    ● **C.** by describing a tornado and explaining how tornadoes form
    ○ **D.** by listing the wind speeds of tornadoes

2. Why is the town of Water Valley, Ohio, mentioned in the introduction?
    ● **F.** to get the reader's attention
    ○ **G.** to explain the illustration
    ○ **H.** to explain the caption
    ○ **J.** to understand the title

3. Which text feature helps you picture the subject?
    ○ **A.** the introduction
    ● **B.** the illustration
    ○ **C.** the title
    ○ **D.** the caption

4. What does the caption tell you?
    ○ **F.** how the people of Water Valley felt
    ● **G.** how a tornado forms
    ○ **H.** how a thundercloud forms
    ○ **J.** what the wind speed is in a tornado

5. What can you learn from the title?
    ○ **A.** that the passage is about Water Valley
    ● **B.** that the passage is about tornadoes
    ○ **C.** that the passage is about clouds
    ○ **D.** that the passage is about storms

Categorize and Classify

Read each passage. Then read each question and fill in the circle next to the best answer.

Group rescues animals from flood waters

During last week's flood in Denton, Pennsylvania, a group of people worked together to save several animals from the rising waters. Five wildlife photographers who were visiting the area organized the rescue effort. The photographers called on game wardens and neighbors to join the search for animals.

First, they rescued a deer trapped on an island created by the floodwaters. Later in the day, they moved five rabbits and three raccoons to higher ground. Lisa Bellows, one of the photographers, said, "We also saved a mother and baby squirrel. I took some great photographs of them for my collection."

1. Based on the passage, in which category do deer, rabbits, and raccoons belong?

    ○ **A.** animals rescued from an island
    ○ **B.** animals photographed by Lisa Bellows
    ● **C.** animals rescued from the flood
    ○ **D.** animals not moved to higher ground

2. Based on the passage, which of the following do **not** fit into the category of people who rescued the animals?

    ○ **F.** game wardens
    ○ **G.** neighbors
    ○ **H.** photographers
    ● **J.** park rangers

Go on

Lyndsey's Vacation

As the storm moved across the coastal town of Rockport, the rain fell harder and harder. Lyndsey couldn't believe that this was happening during her family's vacation. It was the first time they had ever visited a beach town.

Lyndsey heard the roar of the wind and the sound of heavy rain. She listened to the small hotel creak with the force of the strong wind. Mom did not look up from the book she was reading. Dad watched television. Carl, Lyndsey's brother, listened to music through earphones.

Lyndsey looked out the window and saw a branch fall from the tree in the yard and puddles on the sidewalk. As she watched, the wind blew an old soda can past the window. Lyndsey felt sad.

At last the sun came out. Lyndsey and Carl threw on their bathing suits and ran outside. They splashed in the puddles and looked at the colorful flowers in the yard of the hotel. Then they went to the beach to meet their mom and dad.

Lyndsey decided it wasn't such a bad day after all.

3. Based on the passage, which category includes these things: wind, heavy rain, creaking?

- ○ **A.** things near the hotel
- ● **C.** things Lyndsey hears
- ○ **B.** things on television
- ○ **D.** things Carl listens to

4. Based on the passage, which category includes these things: branch, puddles, soda can?

- ○ **F.** things near the beach
- ○ **H.** things Carl sees
- ● **G.** things Lyndsey sees
- ○ **J.** things Dad reads about in the newspaper

5. Based on the passage, which category includes these things: splashing in puddles and looking at flowers?

- ○ **A.** things that Carl did
- ● **C.** things that Lyndsey and Carl did
- ○ **B.** things that Lyndsey did
- ○ **D.** things that the entire family did

STOP

Name _____

Information and Study Skills

Look at the chart below. Then read each question and fill in the circle next to the best answer. *(using graphic aids: maps, globes, charts, tables, and graphs)*

Once a hurricane forms, it is rated in one of five categories on the Saffir-Simpson Hurricane Scale. Here are the categories:

Category	Wind Speed	Effects
1	74–95 mph	Some flooding but generally no damage to buildings
2	96–110 mph	Lots of trees down and minor damage to roofs
3	111–130 mph	Structural damage in houses and destruction of mobile homes; severe flooding
4	131–155 mph	Some roofs ripped off, major damage to buildings
5	greater than 155 mph	Huge damage to most wooden structures

Use the chart to answer these questions. Fill in the circle next to the best answer.

1. According to the chart, how many categories of hurricanes are there?
   ○ **A.** four
   ● **B.** five
   ○ **C.** six
   ○ **D.** seven

2. What are the wind speeds in a Category 2 hurricane?
   ● **F.** 96–110 mph
   ○ **G.** 111–130 mph
   ○ **H.** 131–155 mph
   ○ **J.** greater than 155 mph

3. Which of the following may happen in a Category 3 hurricane?
   ● **A.** Mobile homes may be destroyed.
   ○ **B.** All the buildings in an area may be damaged.
   ○ **C.** Most homes are destroyed.
   ○ **D.** Trees are blown over.

Read each question and fill in the circle next to the best answer.
(using print and electronic reference sources)

4. Which reference would you use to look up the pronunciation of the word *typhoon?*
   ○ **F.** atlas   ● **H.** dictionary
   ○ **G.** thesaurus   ○ **J.** encyclopedia

5. Which reference would you use to find a detailed map of England?
   ○ **A.** encyclopedia   ○ **C.** thesaurus
   ○ **B.** dictionary   ● **D.** atlas

E Name _____

Base Words

Choose the correct base word for each underlined word below.
Fill in the circle next to the best answer.

1. The wind blew for hours without <u>stopping</u>.
   - ○ **A.** stopp
   - ○ **B.** stops
   - ● **C.** stop
   - ○ **D.** stopped

2. Reporters <u>questioned</u> the people who saw the volcano erupt.
   - ○ **F.** quest
   - ○ **G.** questione
   - ○ **H.** questioning
   - ● **J.** question

3. These storm winds were <u>stronger</u> than those of last year.
   - ● **A.** strong
   - ○ **B.** stron
   - ○ **C.** stronge
   - ○ **D.** strongest

4. He <u>watched</u> in horror as the water rose.
   - ● **F.** watch
   - ○ **G.** watcher
   - ○ **H.** watches
   - ○ **J.** watching

5. A waterspout is a tornado that <u>travels</u> over water.
   - ○ **A.** traveled
   - ● **B.** travel
   - ○ **C.** trav
   - ○ **D.** traveling

F Name _____

Syllabication

Choose the correct way to divide each underlined word into syllables.

1. We heard the sound of <u>thunder</u>. *(VCCV pattern)*
    - ● **A.** thun • der
    - ○ **B.** thund • er
    - ○ **C.** thu • nder
    - ○ **D.** th • un • der

2. The plane flew into the eye of the <u>hurricane</u>. *(VCCV pattern)*
    - ○ **F.** hur • ric • ane
    - ○ **G.** hurr • i • cane
    - ○ **H.** hurri • cane
    - ● **J.** hur • ri • cane

3. This <u>climate</u> is very rainy. *(VCV pattern)*
    - ○ **A.** clim • ate
    - ○ **B.** cli • ma • te
    - ● **C.** cli • mate
    - ○ **D.** cl • im • ate

4. The tornado was the town's worst <u>tragedy</u>. *(VCV pattern)*
    - ○ **F.** tra • ge • dy
    - ● **G.** trag • e • dy
    - ○ **H.** tra • gedy
    - ○ **J.** tra • ged • y

5. She saw two broken <u>radios</u> in the middle of the street. *(CVVC pattern)*
    - ○ **A.** rad • i • os
    - ● **B.** ra • di • os
    - ○ **C.** ra • d • ios
    - ○ **D.** r • adi • os

Word Roots: *struct* and *rupt*

Choose the correct meaning for each underlined word. Fill in the circle next to the best answer.

1. The <u>construction</u> of the new dam will begin in August.
    - ● **A.** building
    - ○ **B.** tearing down
    - ○ **C.** changing
    - ○ **D.** moving

2. The safety <u>instructions</u> said not to talk on the phone during a thunderstorm.
    - ○ **F.** a book that tells about storms
    - ○ **G.** a type of phone
    - ○ **H.** someone who writes about safety
    - ● **J.** a list of steps telling how to do or make something

3. The pipe suddenly <u>ruptured</u>, and water poured into the room.
    - ○ **A.** fell over
    - ○ **B.** rolled away
    - ● **C.** broke apart
    - ○ **D.** filled up

4. The earthquake caused widespread <u>destruction</u>.
    - ○ **F.** panic
    - ● **G.** damage
    - ○ **H.** tremors
    - ○ **J.** sadness

5. The news of the storm <u>interrupted</u> my favorite program.
    - ● **A.** broke into
    - ○ **B.** turned off
    - ○ **C.** came after
    - ○ **D.** came at an early hour

Name _____

Spelling

Find the correctly spelled word to complete each sentence.
Fill in the circle beside your answer.

1. The _____ current carried the small raft. *(short i)*
    - ○ **A.** sewift
    - ○ **B.** sweft
    - ● **C.** swift
    - ○ **D.** swieft

2. As I waded into the water, I felt a pain in my _____. *(long i)*
    - ○ **F.** theigh
    - ○ **G.** thye
    - ○ **H.** thei
    - ● **J.** thigh

3. I had never _____ in a tent before. *(short e)*
    - ○ **A.** sleept
    - ○ **B.** sleapt
    - ● **C.** slept
    - ○ **D.** slepth

4. A raccoon _____ my sandwich. *(long o)*
    - ○ **F.** stowl
    - ○ **G.** stol
    - ● **H.** stole
    - ○ **J.** stohl

5. I was thankful to see my _____ group gathered near the picnic benches.
    (the yo͞o sound)
    - ● **A.** youth
    - ○ **B.** yuth
    - ○ **C.** yuoth
    - ○ **D.** yooth

Go on ⟩

6. I could see the top of the pine tree _____ in the breeze. *(long a)*

   ○ **F.** swae

   ○ **G.** swai

   ○ **H.** sweigh

   ● **J.** sway

7. Some friends invited me on a _____ through the woods. *(long o)*

   ● **A.** stroll

   ○ **B.** stroal

   ○ **C.** strole

   ○ **D.** stroul

8. We laughed because we were in such a happy _____. *(o͞o)*

   ○ **F.** muud

   ○ **G.** moode

   ● **H.** mood

   ○ **J.** moud

9. Tonight we plan to sleep in _____ beds. *(short u)*

   ○ **A.** bounk

   ○ **B.** bunck

   ● **C.** bunk

   ○ **D.** buunk

10. We paddled our canoe over to the _____. *(short o)*

   ● **F.** dock

   ○ **G.** dawk

   ○ **H.** dahk

   ○ **J.** dook

Name _____

Vocabulary

Read each question. Fill in the circle next to the best answer.

1. Which word can best replace the underlined word in the following sentence?

   Photographing storms is a very <u>risky</u> job. (*using a thesaurus*)

   ○ **A.** uncertain   ○ **C.** false
   ○ **B.** reliable   ● **D.** dangerous

2. Which word can best replace the underlined word in the following sentence?

   The copilot helps to <u>steer</u> the airplane. (*using a thesaurus*)

   ○ **F.** review   ○ **H.** surround
   ● **G.** guide   ○ **J.** invade

3. Which word can best replace the underlined word in the following sentence?

   She was the gold medal <u>champion</u> of the contest. (*using a thesaurus*)

   ○ **A.** actor   ● **C.** winner
   ○ **B.** historian   ○ **D.** fighter

4. Which set of guide words might appear at the top of a dictionary page on which the word *sketch* is found? (*dictionary: guide words*)

   ● **F.** skate/skew
   ○ **G.** skit/skull
   ○ **H.** skipper/skunk
   ○ **J.** skirt/skittle

5. Which set of guide words might appear at the top of a dictionary page on which the word *damage* is found? (*dictionary: guide words*)

   ○ **A.** dabble/dainty
   ○ **B.** daybreak/dealer
   ● **C.** daily/dangle
   ○ **D.** damp/daring

   Go on ⟩

6. Which word comes first in a dictionary? *(dictionary: alphabetical order)*

    ○ **F.** driver   ○ **H.** drift

    ● **G.** drawing   ○ **J.** drown

7. Which word comes first in a dictionary? *(dictionary: alphabetical order)*

    ○ **A.** trap   ○ **C.** train

    ○ **B.** transfer   ● **D.** track

Read the following dictionary entry and the questions that follow. Fill in the circle next to the best answer.

---

glass (glăs), *n.* **1.** A hard, clear material that is used to make windows and lenses: *The computer screen is made of glass.* **2.** A container to drink from made of glass: *He filled a glass with water.* **3.** The amount a glass can hold: *Pour a glass of milk into the bowl.* **4.** A mirror: *He stared at his reflection in the glass.*

---

8. Which meaning of *glass* is used in this sentence?

    She studied her face in the glass. *(dictionary definitions)*

    ○ **F.** definition 1   ○ **H.** definition 3

    ○ **G.** definition 2   ● **J.** definition 4

9. Which meaning of *glass* is used in this sentence?

    He drank lemonade from a tall glass. *(dictionary definitions)*

    ○ **A.** definition 1   ○ **C.** definition 3

    ● **B.** definition 2   ○ **D.** definition 4

10. Which meaning of *glass* is used in this sentence?

    Add a glass of broth to each pot. *(dictionary definitions)*

    ○ **F.** definition 1   ● **H.** definition 3

    ○ **G.** definition 2   ○ **J.** definition 4

Name _____

Grammar

Read the directions. Then fill in the circle next to the best answer.

1. Choose the exclamatory sentence. *(kinds of sentences)*
   - ○ **A.** My sister was once in a hurricane.
   - ○ **B.** She was visiting our aunt in North Carolina.
   - ● **C.** She saw a tree blow over!
   - ○ **D.** Have you ever been in such a storm?

2. Choose the interrogative sentence. *(kinds of sentences)*
   - ● **F.** Do you know why hurricanes have names?
   - ○ **G.** Naming them helps scientists keep track of the storms.
   - ○ **H.** There once was a hurricane named Betsy.
   - ○ **J.** That's my mother's name!

3. Choose the imperative sentence. *(kinds of sentences)*
   - ○ **A.** Did you hear about the storm last night?
   - ○ **B.** It rained over two inches in one hour.
   - ○ **C.** The wind blew our newspaper down the street.
   - ● **D.** Find the newspaper and bring it back.

4. Choose the declarative sentence. *(kinds of sentences)*
   - ○ **F.** Why can't Grandma come to visit on Saturday?
   - ● **G.** She has to clean up after the storm.
   - ○ **H.** Please go patch the roof.
   - ○ **J.** That will take two days!

5. Choose the complete subject in the following sentence: *(subjects and predicates)*
   The powerful hurricane in Florida caused great destruction.
   - ● **A.** The powerful hurricane in Florida
   - ○ **B.** hurricane
   - ○ **C.** The powerful hurricane
   - ○ **D.** caused great destruction.

Go on ⇨

6. Choose the complete predicate in the following sentence:

The huge tornado destroyed everything in its path. *(subjects and predicates)*

   ○ **F.** The huge tornado   ○ **H.** tornado
   ○ **G.** destroyed everything   ● **J.** destroyed everything in its path.

7. Choose the simple predicate in the following sentence:

The beautiful Mount Fuji last erupted in 1707. *(subjects and predicates)*

   ○ **A.** Mount Fuji last erupted   ○ **C.** The beautiful Mount Fuji
   ● **B.** erupted   ○ **D.** erupted in 1707.

8. Choose the word that best completes the following sentence:

The volcano showed signs of becoming active, _____ people began to leave their homes. *(conjunctions)*

   ○ **F.** but   ● **H.** and
   ○ **G.** or   ○ **J.** except

9. Choose the compound sentence. *(compound sentences)*

   ○ **A.** Scientists, who had watched the volcano for months, said that it could erupt at any time.
   ○ **B.** When the volcano finally erupted, emergency workers were prepared.
   ● **C.** A cloud of ashes rose from the crater, and lava poured down the side of the mountain.
   ○ **D.** The people in nearby towns loaded their belongings into their cars. Then they drove to safety.

10. Choose the sentence in which correct plural nouns are used. *(singular and plural nouns)*

   ○ **F.** The reporter turned in two storys about the weather.
   ○ **G.** She wrote that volcanos are awesome eventes.
   ○ **H.** She said that high windes could rip branchs off trees.
   ● **J.** Her articles were printed in two newspapers.

Name _____

Writing Skills

Choose the group of words that is a complete, correctly written sentence. Fill in the circle next to your answer.

1. ○ **A.** Had no way of knowing that a storm was coming. *(correcting sentence*
   ○ **B.** Felt a few raindrops falling. *fragments)*
   ● **C.** Then hail began to fall from the sky.
   ○ **D.** The car and roof.

2. ● **F.** The earthquake shook the house. *(correcting sentence fragments)*
   ○ **G.** Glasses and plates from the shelves.
   ○ **H.** Fell down all around us.
   ○ **J.** The Smith's house on the corner.

3. ○ **A.** The day the dam on the Harris River broke. *(correcting sentence*
   ○ **B.** To rebuild some of the neighborhoods. *fragments)*
   ○ **C.** New rules from the government about flooding.
   ● **D.** Many people had to leave their homes behind.

Choose the sentence that is capitalized and punctuated correctly. Fill in the circle next to the best answer.

4. ● **F.** Mt. Washington is known for its extreme weather. *(capitalizing and*
   ○ **G.** winds of 75 miles per hour are common. *punctuating*
   ○ **H.** When do the winds reach maximum speed. *sentences)*
   ○ **J.** Ranger Station is at the top of the mountain?

5. ○ **A.** the volcano on the small island erupted. *(capitalizing and punctuating sentences)*
   ○ **B.** The hot orange lava rolled slowly toward the sea
   ● **C.** A helicopter flew near the crater.
   ○ **D.** Mr. Wright took spectacular photographs of the sight?

Give It All You've Got

Level 5, Theme 2

Theme Skills Test Record

Student _____ Date _____

Student Record Form

	Possible Score	Criterion Score	Student Score
Part A: Fact and Opinion	5	4	
Part B: Story Structure	5	4	
Part C: Predicting Outcomes	5	4	
Part D: Topic, Main Idea, and Supporting Details	5	4	
Part E: Information and Study Skills	5	4	
Part F: Compound Words	5	4	
Part G: Roots *spec/t* and *opt*	5	4	
Part H: Suffixes *-ward* and *-ous*	5	4	
Part I: Suffixes *-ive* and *-ic*	5	4	
Part J: Spelling	10	8	
Part K: Vocabulary	10	8	
Part L: Grammar	10	8	
Part M: Writing Skills	5	4	
TOTAL	80	64	
Total Student Score x 1.25 =			%

Name _____

Fact and Opinion

Read the passage. Then read each question and fill in the circle next to the best answer.

Clementine Hunter, Artist

Clementine Hunter was born in Louisiana in 1885. As a girl, she picked cotton on a large farm called a plantation. As an adult, she worked in the plantation's laundry and kitchen. Although her work was difficult, Clementine enjoyed watching the things that happened around her. She loved to see people dancing and girls picking flowers. She watched children playing and dogs wagging their tails. It seemed that she saw interesting sights everywhere she looked.

One day a visitor to the plantation left behind some old tubes of paint. Clementine wanted to try out the paints, but she didn't have anything to paint on. She began to search for something to use as a canvas. Soon she found a window shade in the trash. In no time, she had created a charming painting on the shade.

Clementine was in her fifties when this happened. Even though she loved to paint, she could not take formal art lessons. This didn't stop her. She began to paint whenever she got the chance. She painted lively scenes of people cooking food, playing games, and getting married. She painted on paper bags, scraps of wood, bottles, and even on old pots. When she died at the age of 101, she had created over 4,000 paintings.

Over the years people in nearby communities began to hear about Clementine's paintings. She became the first African-American painter to show her artwork at the New Orleans Museum of Art. Today, many experts feel that her paintings are the work of an extremely talented artist. Some even feel that she was as skilled as a well-known painter named Grandma Moses. People who collect her paintings believe that she is one of the best painters ever.

1. Which of the following statements is an opinion?
   - ○ **A.** Clementine picked cotton as a young girl.
   - ○ **B.** Clementine began painting when she was in her fifties.
   - ● **C.** Clementine was an extremely talented artist.
   - ○ **D.** Clementine used a window shade to make her first painting.

2. Which of the following statements is a fact?
   - ● **F.** Clementine died at the age of 101.
   - ○ **G.** Clementine's first painting was charming.
   - ○ **H.** It seemed that Clementine saw interesting sights everywhere she looked.
   - ○ **J.** Clementine is one of the best painters ever.

3. How do you know that the following statement is a fact?

   Clementine was the first African-American painter to display her work at the New Orleans Museum of Art.
   - ○ **A.** The author is reliable.
   - ● **B.** The statement can be proven.
   - ○ **C.** Detailed information is given.
   - ○ **D.** The statement is easy to believe.

4. Which of these statements is an opinion?
   - ○ **F.** Clementine painted on paper bags, scraps of wood, bottles, and even on old pots.
   - ○ **G.** When she died, Clementine had created over 4,000 paintings.
   - ○ **H.** Clementine was born in Louisiana in 1885.
   - ● **J.** Clementine was as skilled as Grandma Moses.

5. Which word in this sentence signals an opinion?

   People who collect her paintings believe that she is one of the best painters ever.
   - ○ **A.** People
   - ● **C.** believe
   - ○ **B.** collect
   - ○ **D.** ever

Name _____

Story Structure

Read the passage. Then read each question and fill in the circle next to the best answer.

The Recital

Chad finished playing his favorite piece on the piano. Then he looked up at his piano teacher.

"How lovely, Chad! I can tell that you've been practicing," exclaimed Mrs. Franklin. "Now, I have a surprise for you. In two weeks, we're going to have a recital at the Parkdale Library. You'll be able to play your song for your family. The other students and their families will attend, too."

On the way home Chad kicked a stone from the path. He thought about how awful it would be to play in front of other people. "I just don't think I can do it," he decided.

That afternoon Chad asked his sister Cara to help him think of a way to get out of the recital. "It won't be so bad," she told him. Then she invited him to come with her to the library.

After they had been there awhile, Cara said, "Let's go find the piano. As many times as I've been here, I've never seen it." The librarian directed them to a room on the second floor.

The shiny, black piano was the most beautiful one Chad had ever seen. As he ran his hand lightly over the keys, Cara sat down in a chair. "Go ahead, Chad. Just pretend that I'm not even here," she urged.

Chad began playing. Within minutes he was carried away by the beautiful sound of the instrument. When he finished, Cara's clapping startled him. Later, Chad and Cara stopped at the drugstore. Mr. Turner, who owned the store, greeted them. His daughter, Melissa, was one of Mrs. Franklin's students.

"Chad, I can't wait to hear you play at the recital," said Mr. Turner. Chad looked at Cara. He thought about the piano and how much his mother and father would enjoy hearing him play it.

"Thanks," replied Chad. "I think you'll really like the piece I've chosen to play."

1. Who is the main character in this story?
- ○ **A.** Mrs. Franklin
- ○ **B.** Mr. Turner
- ○ **C.** Cara
- ● **D.** Chad

2. What problem does Chad have?
- ○ **F.** He doesn't want to go to the library with Cara.
- ● **G.** He feels nervous about his piano recital.
- ○ **H.** He doesn't like his piano teacher.
- ○ **J.** He has not practiced his piano piece enough.

3. Who helps Chad solve his problem?
- ● **A.** Cara
- ○ **B.** Mrs. Franklin
- ○ **C.** Chad's mother
- ○ **D.** Melissa

4. Where does Chad solve his problem?
- ○ **F.** at Chad's school
- ● **G.** in the library
- ○ **H.** on the way home from his lesson
- ○ **J.** in Cara's bedroom

5. Which is the first **important** event?
- ○ **A.** Chad walks home.
- ● **B.** Mrs. Franklin tells Chad about the recital.
- ○ **C.** Chad kicks a stone.
- ○ **D.** Cara invites Chad to the library.

Name _____

Predicting Outcomes

Read the passage. Then read each question and fill in the circle next to the best answer.

Counting to Five

Both Lisa and Charlotte had brown hair and green eyes. They were both friendly, and they liked the same subjects in school. Both girls played soccer and liked to swim. If one girl tried something new, the other one always tried it, too. The main difference between the two girls was that Lisa was sometimes less patient than Charlotte.

One day before soccer practice, Lisa and Charlotte went swimming at the recreation center. While they were there, Lisa decided that she wanted to jump off the high diving board. She had jumped off the low board many times, but the high board had always scared her. Charlotte had never jumped from the high board either. "I know I can do it," Lisa said to herself.

Lisa told Charlotte what she planned to do. Then she slowly climbed the ladder while Charlotte watched. She walked nervously to the end of the board and looked down. The water seemed to be miles below. For just a minute, she thought about going back down the ladder. Then she decided that it might be easier if she closed her eyes.

From the ground, Charlotte saw Lisa squeeze her eyes shut, then open them quickly. "It's too scary to do this with my eyes closed," Lisa yelled to Charlotte. "I wouldn't know when I was going to hit the water."

"I know a trick," Charlotte called back. "Try counting very slowly to five. That always helps me do scary things."

Lisa began to count. "One. . . Two. . . Three. . . ." On the third count, Lisa leapt from the board and splashed into the water. When she came to the surface, she was laughing. "Oh, Charlotte, that was so much fun! From now on, I'll always count when I try something new. Only I'll always have to stop at three because I'm not as patient as you are."

1. What does Lisa probably say to Charlotte after the story ends?
   ○ **A.** "Let's have a snack."   ○ **C.** "The water feels great."
   ● **B.** "Now, you try it."   ○ **D.** "You're more patient."

2. Which of these will Charlotte probably do the next time she tries something new?
   ○ **F.** hold her breath   ○ **H.** hold Lisa's hand
   ○ **G.** close her eyes   ● **J.** count to five

3. Which sentence from the story might help readers predict that Lisa won't count all the way to five before jumping?
   ○ **A.** They were on the same soccer team, and they both liked to swim.
   ○ **B.** From the ground, Charlotte saw Lisa squeeze her eyes shut, then open them quickly.
   ● **C.** The main difference between the two girls was that Lisa was sometimes less patient than Charlotte.
   ○ **D.** "From now on, I'll always count when I try something new."

4. Which detail from the story helps readers predict that Lisa will find the courage to jump off the board?
   ● **F.** She says, "I know I can do it."
   ○ **G.** She walks slowly to the end of the board.
   ○ **H.** The water looks like it's miles below her.
   ○ **J.** She closes her eyes before she jumps.

5. Which lesson from your own experience might have helped you predict that Lisa would find the courage to jump off the high board?
   ● **A.** A good friend can help you to be brave.
   ○ **B.** It's fun to do things with a good friend.
   ○ **C.** Good friends are hard to find.
   ○ **D.** You can share your problems with a friend.

Topic, Main Idea, and Supporting Details

Read the passage. Then read each question and fill in the circle next to the best answer.

How to Clean Your Room

Cleaning a room doesn't have to be a hard or boring job. In fact, there are many ways to make this task easy and fun.

Listening to music can add fun to work. Before you start to clean your room, turn on a radio or put on your favorite CD. Be sure to choose music that has a lively beat. This will brighten your mood, and it will help the time go by quickly.

Picking up the trash in your room is a good place to start. This step is really quite easy. First, find a wastebasket or paper bag. Moving in time to the music, go around the room and pick up all the trash. When you finish, empty the wastebasket into a trash can.

Putting large objects away will make a room appear cleaner. Look around and find the four largest objects that need to be put away. Put these objects where they belong. In an instant your room will seem neater and your job smaller.

Next, put everything that is out of place into piles. You might place all the clothes in one pile, all the toys in another, and all the books and magazines in another. Plan ahead as you do this. That is, put the pile of toys near the toy box and the pile of clothes near the closet. Don't forget to sing along to the music while you work.

Finally, go through each pile and put everything where it belongs. Put the dirty clothes in the clothes hamper and hang up the clean clothes. Neatly arrange the books on the book shelf and put the toys in the toy box. Last, take a quick look around to be sure that you didn't forget anything. Be proud of a job well done.

1. What is the topic of this passage?
   - ○ **A.** how to pick up trash while moving to music
   - ○ **B.** how to have fun while putting things in piles
   - ● **C.** how to clean up a room and have fun
   - ○ **D.** how to find four large objects in a messy room

2. Which sentence from the passage states the main idea of the second paragraph?
   - ● **F.** Listening to music can add fun to work.
   - ○ **G.** Before you start to clean your room, turn on a radio or put on your favorite CD.
   - ○ **H.** Be sure to choose music that has a lively beat.
   - ○ **J.** This will brighten your mood, and it will help the time go by quickly.

3. Which detail supports the idea that picking up trash is a good place to begin?
   - ● **A.** This step is really quite easy.
   - ○ **B.** Put the toys in the toy box.
   - ○ **C.** Be sure not to forget anything.
   - ○ **D.** Cleaning a room doesn't have to be boring.

4. Which detail supports the idea that cleaning your room can be fun?
   - ○ **F.** Find a wastebasket or paper bag.
   - ● **G.** Don't forget to sing along as you work.
   - ○ **H.** Take a quick look around to be sure that you didn't forget anything.
   - ○ **J.** Be proud of a job well done.

5. Which sentence from the passage states the main idea of the fourth paragraph?
   - ○ **A.** Look around and find the four largest objects that need to be put away.
   - ○ **B.** Put these objects where they belong.
   - ○ **C.** In an instant your room will seem neater and your job smaller.
   - ● **D.** Putting large objects away will make a room appear cleaner.

STOP

Name _____

Information and Study Skills *(select the appropriate reference source)*

Read each question and fill in the circle next to the best answer.

1. Which of these would you use if you needed to find a friend's address?
   - ○ **A.** Thesaurus
   - ○ **B.** Encyclopedia
   - ○ **C.** Atlas
   - ● **D.** Telephone Directory

2. Which of these would you use if you wanted to find out who won gold medals in the Olympic Games in 1972?
   - ○ **F.** Dictionary
   - ● **G.** Almanac
   - ○ **H.** Atlas
   - ○ **J.** Thesaurus

3. Which of these would you use to find out where China is located?
   - ● **A.** Atlas
   - ○ **B.** Telephone Directory
   - ○ **C.** Encyclopedia
   - ○ **D.** Dictionary

4. Which of these would you use to look up the pronunciation of the word *icicle*?
   - ● **F.** Dictionary
   - ○ **G.** Almanac
   - ○ **H.** Encyclopedia
   - ○ **J.** Thesaurus

5. Which of these would you use to find a word that is the opposite in meaning of the word *stroll*?
   - ○ **A.** Dictionary
   - ○ **B.** Atlas
   - ● **C.** Thesaurus
   - ○ **D.** Almanac

STOP

Compound Words

Choose the compound word that has the same meaning as the underlined part of each sentence. Fill in the circle next to the best answer.

1. My father took a <u>tool that shines light</u> on our night hike.
   - ○ **A.** lantern
   - ● **B.** flashlight
   - ○ **C.** light bulb
   - ○ **D.** candle

2. We left the tent before <u>the sun came up</u>.
   - ○ **F.** morning
   - ○ **G.** sunset
   - ● **H.** sunrise
   - ○ **J.** dusk

3. I put a <u>tool I use to brush my teeth</u> in my pocket.
   - ○ **A.** brush
   - ● **B.** toothbrush
   - ○ **C.** toothpick
   - ○ **D.** dental floss

4. We planned to walk to the park ranger's <u>main office</u>.
   - ○ **F.** headlight
   - ○ **G.** store
   - ○ **H.** lodge
   - ● **J.** headquarters

5. When we got there, my father bought a <u>paper with the day's news</u>.
   - ● **A.** newspaper
   - ○ **B.** newsprint
   - ○ **C.** newscast
   - ○ **D.** magazine

STOP

Roots *spec/t* and *opt*

Choose the correct meaning for each underlined word.
Fill in the circle next to the best answer.

1. Before the race the coach <u>inspects</u> the track.
   - ● **A.** looks at carefully
   - ○ **B.** runs around
   - ○ **C.** quickly cleans up
   - ○ **D.** smoothes out

2. Heat waves rising from the track create an <u>optical</u> illusion.
   - ● **F.** having to do with vision
   - ○ **G.** having to do with runners
   - ○ **H.** interesting
   - ○ **J.** happening over and over

3. The <u>spectators</u> cheer as the runners cross the finish line.
   - ○ **A.** coaches for a winning team
   - ○ **B.** people who keep scores
   - ● **C.** people who watch an event
   - ○ **D.** athletes who compete

4. Mr. Vegas cannot see the scores without his <u>spectacles</u>.
   - ○ **F.** scoreboards
   - ○ **G.** words
   - ○ **H.** camera
   - ● **J.** eyeglasses

5. Mr. Vegas decides to see an <u>optician</u> the next day.
   - ○ **A.** a person who fills orders for medicine
   - ● **B.** a person who checks people's eyes
   - ○ **C.** a person who assists a doctor
   - ○ **D.** a person who fixes people's bones

Name _____

Suffixes -*ward* and -*ous*

Choose the correct meaning for each underlined word.
Fill in the circle next to the best answer.

1. My brother was <u>envious</u> when I got new soccer shoes.
   - ● **A.** full of envy
   - ○ **B.** wanting envy
   - ○ **C.** the opposite of envy
   - ○ **D.** without envy

2. I kicked the ball <u>upward</u>, and it sailed over the fence.
   - ○ **F.** the opposite of up
   - ○ **G.** without moving up
   - ○ **H.** not moving up
   - ● **J.** moving up

3. The shopkeeper was <u>furious</u> when the ball broke a window.
   - ○ **A.** the opposite of fury
   - ○ **B.** without fury
   - ● **C.** full of fury
   - ○ **D.** having little fury

4. My <u>adventurous</u> aunt went river rafting last summer.
   - ○ **F.** without adventure
   - ● **G.** full of adventure
   - ○ **H.** afraid of adventure
   - ○ **J.** the opposite of adventure

5. Brightly colored leaves drifted <u>downward</u> on the chilly fall day.
   - ● **A.** moving down
   - ○ **B.** the opposite of down
   - ○ **C.** not moving down
   - ○ **D.** without moving down

STOP

Name _____

Suffixes *-ive* and *-ic*

Choose the correct meaning for each underlined word.
Fill in the circle next to the best answer.

1. Larry is a <u>creative</u> painter.
   - ● **A.** having the ability to create
   - ○ **B.** without the ability to create
   - ○ **C.** learning how to create
   - ○ **D.** one who is unable to create

2. Our <u>poetic</u> parrot loves to make up rhymes.
   - ○ **F.** unlike a poet
   - ● **G.** like a poet
   - ○ **H.** unable to be a poet
   - ○ **J.** without a poet

3. The house has an <u>expansive</u> view of the valley.
   - ○ **A.** expanding upward
   - ○ **B.** not expanding
   - ● **C.** expanding in all directions
   - ○ **D.** expanding very little

4. My <u>athletic</u> brother can run, jump, and swim.
   - ○ **F.** unable to be an athlete
   - ○ **G.** with an athlete
   - ○ **H.** unlike an athlete
   - ● **J.** like an athlete

5. Wren is an <u>expressive</u> speaker.
   - ○ **A.** lacking the ability to express ideas clearly
   - ● **B.** having the ability to express ideas clearly
   - ○ **C.** being filled with ideas to express clearly
   - ○ **D.** one who has the ability to express ideas clearly

Name _____

Spelling

Find the correctly spelled word to complete each sentence.
Fill in the circle beside your answer.

1. We are expecting almost a _____ people at the fair. *(/ou/)*
   ○ **A.** thousend
   ● **B.** thousand
   ○ **C.** thowsand
   ○ **D.** thoosand

2. In this booklet you will find an _____ schedule of fair events. *(compound words)*
   ○ **F.** up-to date
   ○ **G.** up to date
   ● **H.** up-to-date
   ○ **J.** upto date

3. The winner of the drawing will receive a _____ necklace. *(/ûr/)*
   ○ **A.** paerl
   ○ **B.** purl
   ● **C.** pearl
   ○ **D.** pirol

4. The necklace is _____ a lot of money. *(/ûr/)*
   ● **F.** worth
   ○ **G.** wirth
   ○ **H.** werth
   ○ **J.** wearth

5. On opening night, Ms. Kennedy _____ tickets from a long roll. *(/ôr/)*
   ● **A.** tore
   ○ **B.** toure
   ○ **C.** toar
   ○ **D.** toor

Go on ⟩

6. If you get thirsty, you can _____ at the snack booth for a cold drink. *(/ô/)*

- ○ **F.** paws
- ● **G.** pause
- ○ **H.** poss
- ○ **J.** paase

7. The decorations for the booths show Lara's _____ for using color. *(/âr/)*

- ○ **A.** flayre
- ○ **B.** flaire
- ○ **C.** flare
- ● **D.** flair

8. Children may _____ paint on a large poster board near the wading pool.

(/îr/)

- ● **F.** smear
- ○ **G.** smeer
- ○ **H.** smeir
- ○ **J.** smere

9. They can also watch adults _____ animal figures from bars of soap. *(/är/)*

- ○ **A.** carrve
- ○ **B.** cawrve
- ● **C.** carve
- ○ **D.** caurve

10. The children's area is always very _____! *(/oi/)*

- ○ **F.** noeesy
- ○ **G.** nossy
- ● **H.** noisy
- ○ **J.** noesy

Name _____

Vocabulary

Read the sentences and answer the questions.
Fill in the circle next to the best answer.

1. Which word is not related to the others? *(word families)*
   ○ **A.** divide   ○ **C.** dividend
   ○ **B.** division   ● **D.** divers

2. Which word is not related to the others? *(word families)*
   ○ **F.** number   ○ **H.** numerous
   ● **G.** nimble   ○ **J.** numeral

3. Which word is not related to the others? *(word families)*
   ○ **A.** study   ○ **C.** studious
   ○ **B.** student   ● **D.** stuck

4. Which word best completes the sentence?   *(homophones)*
   My favorite snack is a _____.
   ○ **F.** pair   ● **H.** pear
   ○ **G.** pare   ○ **J.** peer

5. Which word best completes the sentence?   *(homophones)*
   The _____ along the Alaskan coast lasted two days.
   ● **A.** cruise   ○ **C.** cruse
   ○ **B.** crews   ○ **D.** croose

6. Which word best completes the sentence?   *(homophones)*

The scratch on my hand took three days to _____.

   ○ **F.** he'll   ○ **H.** hele

   ○ **G.** heel   ● **J.** heal

7. Which word best completes the sentence?   *(homophones)*

Please hand me a _____, a hammer, and a nail.

   ○ **A.** bored   ○ **C.** boared

   ○ **B.** boored   ● **D.** board

Read each dictionary entry. Circle the answer choice with the correct stress.

8. as • ter • oid (as′ tə roid′) *n.* One of many small planets that orbit the sun.

                                                    (dictionary: syllabication)

   ● **F.** AS/te/roid

   ○ **G.** as/TE/roid

   ○ **H.** as/TER/oid

   ○ **J.** as/te/ROID

9. ap • pli • cant (ap′ li kənt) *n.* A person who applies for something.

                                                    (dictionary: syllabication)

   ● **A.** AP/pli/cant

   ○ **B.** ap/pli/CANT

   ○ **C.** ap/PLI/cant

   ○ **D.** APP/li/cant

10. i • mag • i • na • tion (i maj′ ə na′ shən) *adj.* The ability of the brain to picture things that are not real. *(dictionary: syllabication)*

   ○ **F.** I/mag/i/na/tion

   ○ **G.** i/MAG/i/na/tion

   ● **H.** i/mag/i/NA/tion

   ○ **J.** i/mag/i/na/TION

Name _____

Grammar

Follow the directions. Then fill in the circle next to the best answer.

1. Choose a sentence that does **not** contain a helping verb. *(helping verbs)*

    ○ **A.** Erica is climbing the steepest trail.
    ○ **B.** She will go to the very highest peak.
    ● **C.** She wants a photograph of the valley below.
    ○ **D.** Has she ever made the climb before?

2. Choose a sentence that does **not** contain a linking verb. *(linking verbs)*

    ○ **F.** Sal is an experienced hiker.
    ○ **G.** She still feels nervous before hikes.
    ● **H.** She will talk to the group this evening.
    ○ **J.** Sal is not a nervous speaker.

3. Choose a sentence that contains a predicate noun. *(linking verbs)*

    ○ **A.** Hoover will lead the group hike on Saturday.
    ○ **B.** He plans to leave from Lookout Point.
    ● **C.** He is an expert on the plants of the region.
    ○ **D.** He tells the hikers about animals, too.

4. Choose a sentence that contains a predicate adjective. *(linking verbs)*

    ● **F.** Hillary was frightened by reports of a bear near the campground.
    ○ **G.** She decided to find out if the reports were true.
    ○ **H.** She spoke to a park ranger stationed near the canyon.
    ○ **J.** He told her not to worry.

5. Choose a sentence that does **not** contain a direct object. *(direct objects)*

    ○ **A.** Alison hit the ball into the field.
    ● **B.** Alison ran around the bases.
    ○ **C.** Matt caught the ball in his glove.
    ○ **D.** Matt held the ball in the air.

Go on ⇨

6. Choose the sentence that does **not** contain an action verb.   *(action verbs)*

    ● **F.** Aunt Lorraine is my favorite relative.

    ○ **G.** She walks four miles every day.

    ○ **H.** She reads at least four books each month.

    ○ **J.** She plays tennis with me every week.

Fill in the circle next to the sentence that is written correctly.
(common and proper nouns, singular and plural possessive nouns, verb tenses)

7. ○ **A.** My aunt, who lives in roanoke, Virginia, loves to travel.

     ● **B.** Last year she took a trip to Texas and New Mexico.

     ○ **C.** She visited a mission in San antonio and a pueblo in Santa fe.

     ○ **D.** She liked the swimming in the gulf of Mexico best of all.

8. ○ **F.** Over 500 people have signed up to run in the Womens' 5K Run on Saturday.

     ○ **G.** I love to hear the sound of hundreds of runner's feet at the start of the race.

     ○ **H.** The runners will help raise money for the communitys' children.

     ● **J.** Some of the money will be used to buy children's books for the library.

9. ○ **A.** The coach's conference was held last month.

     ○ **B.** One athletes' speech lasted two hours.

     ● **C.** The meeting for men's soccer was a big success.

     ○ **D.** One teams' coach brought T-shirts for all.

10. ○ **F.** Last month my sister and I will learn a new sport.

     ● **G.** We watched our friends at the skating rink two weeks ago.

     ○ **H.** Next week I rent two pairs of ice skates.

     ○ **J.** Yesterday my sister and I nervously glide onto the ice.

Name _____

Writing Skills

Read each paragraph and answer the questions that follow. Fill in the circle next to the best answer. *(paraphrasing)*

The members of the basketball team gathered in the locker room before the big game. They greeted one another quietly. Suzanne felt a knot in the pit of her stomach. Her palms were sweaty. The coach came in and the players looked at each other. The coach said, "We're going to win this one for sure!"

1. Which of these best restates how Suzanne felt?
   - ○ **A.** Her stomach felt odd.
   - ○ **B.** She was worried about her sweaty palms.
   - ● **C.** She was nervous.
   - ○ **D.** She wished the other players would speak loudly.

2. In paraphrasing the above paragraph, what information would you **not** include?
   - ○ **F.** The players gathered in the locker room.
   - ● **G.** The players looked at each other.
   - ○ **H.** It was the day of a big game.
   - ○ **J.** The coach was sure the team would win.

Jonathan works at the community library on Saturdays. He helps people choose books and checks the books out. He also straightens the shelves and enters information into the computer. His favorite part of the job is discussing books with the library's visitors.

3. Which of these best combines the ideas in the passage?
   - ● **A.** Jonathan does various jobs at the library on Saturdays.
   - ○ **B.** Jonathan's favorite job at the library is talking about books.
   - ○ **C.** Jonathan sometimes enters information in the library's computer.
   - ○ **D.** Jonathan helps visitors to the library choose books.

Choose the best way to combine each pair of sentences.
Fill in the circle next to your answer. *(combining sentences with helping verbs)*

4. Lucy had washed her face. She had brushed her teeth.
   - ● **F.** Lucy had washed her face and brushed her teeth.
   - ○ **G.** Lucy had washed her face and Lucy had brushed her teeth.
   - ○ **H.** Lucy had washed her face, brushed her teeth.
   - ○ **J.** Lucy had washed her face, she had brushed her teeth.

5. My brother Randy could drive us to the movie. He could see the movie with us.
   - ○ **A.** My brother Randy could drive us to the movie, and he could see the movie with us.
   - ○ **B.** My brother Randy could drive us to the movie and then could see the movie with us.
   - ○ **C.** My brother Randy could drive us to the movie and could see the movie with us.
   - ● **D.** My brother Randy could drive us to the movie and see the movie with us.

Voices of the Revolution

Level 5, Theme 3

Theme Skills Test Record

Student _____ Date _____

Student Record Form

	Possible Score	Criterion Score	Student Score
Part A: Author's Viewpoint	5	4	
Part B: Cause and Effect	5	4	
Part C: Following Directions	5	4	
Part D: Information and Study Skills	5	4	
Part E: Possessives and Contractions	5	4	
Part F: Syllabication: VCCV and VCV Patterns	5	4	
Part G: Prefixes *sub-* and *sur-*	5	4	
Part H: Spelling	10	8	
Part I: Vocabulary	10	8	
Part J: Grammar	10	8	
Part K: Writing Skills	5	4	
TOTAL	70	56	
Total Student Score x 1.43 =			%

Author's Viewpoint

Read the passage. Then read each question and fill in the circle next to the best answer.

Sybil Ludington

On a cold night in 1777, two thousand British soldiers attacked the town of Danbury, Connecticut. Danbury was very important to the colonial army because it was a storage place for food, clothing, and medicine. Unfortunately, only 150 colonial soldiers were available to defend the town. The small army needed help!

A messenger quickly left on horseback to ask Colonel Henry Ludington to bring more troops. However, when the rider arrived at Ludington's farm, he learned that Ludington's men had gone home.

Who could round up the soldiers in the dead of night? Ludington thought of his 16-year-old daughter, Sybil. He knew she could do this dangerous job. In an instant, Sybil saddled her horse Star and rode into the frozen dark. She bravely galloped from farm to farm. She followed twisting, muddy roads across the countryside. Along the way, she shouted the news of the attack. She warned families to be ready to flee if the British should come their way.

Sybil arrived home early the next morning. When she got there she saw more than 400 men preparing to leave for the twenty-five-mile journey to Danbury. Colonel Ludington was very grateful that she had helped.

Today, people remember Sybil's courageous ride. A statue of Sybil and Star stands in the town of Carmel, Connecticut. Sybil has also been honored by having her picture on a postage stamp.

Go on ⟹

1. What is the author's viewpoint in this article?

   ○ **A.** Sybil's ride was the most important event in the American Revolution.
   ○ **B.** Ludington's soldiers should have been ready for battle.
   ○ **C.** Sybil was too young to make such a dangerous ride.
   ● **D.** Sybil Ludington's bravery helped the colonial soldiers.

2. Which statement reflects the author's opinion?

   ● **F.** Sybil Ludington was a very brave girl.
   ○ **G.** Danbury was a storage place for food, clothing, and medicine.
   ○ **H.** More than 400 men went to help the troops in Danbury.
   ○ **J.** A statue of Sybil and Star stands in the town of Carmel.

3. How do you know that the following statement is a fact, and not the author's viewpoint?

   On a cold night in Connecticut in 1777, two thousand British soldiers attacked the town of Danbury, Connecticut.

   ○ **A.** The author is reliable.
   ● **B.** The statement can be proven.
   ○ **C.** Detailed information is given.
   ○ **D.** The statement is easy to believe.

4. Why did the author most likely write this article?

   ○ **F.** to entertain the reader with a story about a girl and a horse
   ● **G.** to inform the reader about events during the colonial period
   ○ **H.** to describe the Connecticut countryside
   ○ **J.** to persuade the reader to visit the statue of Sybil

5. Which of these phrases shows that the author respects Sybil Ludington?

   ○ **A.** shouted the news
   ○ **B.** muddy roads
   ● **C.** dangerous job
   ○ **D.** twenty-five-mile journey

STOP

Name _____

Cause and Effect

Read the passage. Then read each question and fill in the circle next to the best answer.

Just Like Father

Jeremy watched as his father poured the British soldier a drink of water. The soldier hurriedly drank the water and left. "A simple 'Thank you' would have been nice," Jeremy thought grumpily.

Jeremy's father owned an inn in Boston. Months earlier, King George had decided to send soldiers from England to the colonies. The king had ordered the colonists to provide the soldiers food and housing. As a result, Jeremy's father worked very hard. In return for this work, he received only a little money from the city.

After the British soldier drank the water, he walked into the street to join his regiment for inspection. Each morning every soldier had to shave, powder his hair with flour, and polish his boots. Soldiers who did not pass inspection were punished.

As the soldier walked along, a colonist ran by shouting angrily, "Go home, Redcoat!" Most colonists hated having British soldiers in their towns. The soldiers' presence made the tension between England and the colonies worse.

The soldier grumbled, "I hate this job! The colonists hate me, and I have to wear this hot and itchy red jacket. For this, I only get paid eight pence a day! I wish I was back in London!"

When the soldier returned to the inn that evening, Jeremy was struck by the very sad expression on the soldier's face. Instead of a soldier in uniform, Jeremy saw a human being with feelings. "Good evening, sir," Jeremy said.

The warm greeting lifted the soldier's spirits. Jeremy and the soldier began to talk. The soldier told Jeremy about the son he had left behind in London. Later, when Jeremy went to bed, he thought about the British soldiers. "They're men struggling to make their way, just like Father," he decided.

Go on ▷

1. Why did Jeremy's father provide food and housing for British soldiers?
   ○ **A.** King George offered to pay him well for several rooms at the inn.
   ● **B.** King George ordered the colonists to provide the soldiers room and board.
   ○ **C.** King George asked all innkeepers in Boston to help the British soldiers.
   ○ **D.** King George sent Jeremy's father a letter asking him for his help.

2. Why did the colonist shout at the British soldier to go home?
   ○ **F.** The British soldier didn't thank Jeremy's father for the drink of water.
   ○ **G.** The British soldier didn't have his boots polished.
   ● **H.** The British soldiers' presence made the tensions in Boston worse.
   ○ **J.** The British soldier didn't like his job.

3. For British soldiers, which was an effect of not passing inspection?
   ● **A.** They were punished.
   ○ **B.** They were fired.
   ○ **C.** They were forced to work in an inn.
   ○ **D.** They had to apologize to a British officer.

4. Which of these was an effect of the conversation between Jeremy and the soldier?
   ○ **F.** Jeremy began to hate British soldiers.
   ○ **G.** Jeremy wanted to become a British soldier.
   ● **H.** Jeremy began to understand the British soldiers.
   ○ **J.** Jeremy became angry with his father.

5. Which of these was a reason that the British soldier did not like his job?
   ○ **A.** He did not like being in Boston.
   ○ **B.** He did not like carrying a gun.
   ○ **C.** He did not like not going to school.
   ● **D.** He did not get much money.

STOP

Name _____

Following Directions

Read the passage. Then read each question and fill in the circle next to the best answer.

Make a Kite

You probably know that Benjamin Franklin once flew a kite in a thunderstorm. He did this because he had a hunch that the lightning he saw during the storms was electricity. When he received a shock from a key that he had placed on the string, he knew he was right. Now follow these steps to make a kite of your own.

- First, find two sticks. One of the sticks should be about eight inches shorter than the other one.
- Place the two sticks on top of one another in a cross shape. Tie a piece of string in a knot at the place where the two sticks meet.
- With an adult's help, cut a small notch into both ends of each stick.
- Slide one piece of string through all four notches. Pull the string tight and knot the ends together. Now you've made the kite's frame.
- Place the frame onto a large piece of paper. Cut the paper about half an inch away from the frame all the way around.
- Glue around the edge of the paper, and fold it over so that it covers the string and sticks to the paper inside the frame. Now you've covered the kite's frame.
- Cut a long piece of string that equals the length of the short and longer sticks together.
- Tie one end of the string around the top point of the kite. Make a loop one third of the way down the top stick. (Later, you will tie the kite's tail to this loop). Tie the other end of the string to the bottom of the kite. Cut off any extra string. You've just made the bridle.
- Measure a piece of string that is at least five times as long as the kite. Tie this string, called the kite line, to the loop that you made in the last step.
- Attach ribbon or crepe paper to make the tail of the kite.
- Now the kite is ready to go!

1. What is the first step in making the kite?
    ○ **A.** Make a cross shape with the two sticks.
    ○ **B.** Cover the kite frame with paper.
    ● **C.** Find two sticks.
    ○ **D.** Tie ribbon or crepe paper to make the tail.

2. What is the difference in length between the two sticks?
    ● **F.** about eight inches
    ○ **G.** about half an inch
    ○ **H.** about five inches
    ○ **J.** about two inches

3. What should you use to attach the paper to the frame?
    ○ **A.** string
    ○ **B.** tape
    ○ **C.** ribbon or crepe paper
    ● **D.** glue

4. Where should an adult make the kite's notches?
    ○ **F.** around the edges of the paper
    ● **G.** at the ends of both sticks
    ○ **H.** at the knot in the middle
    ○ **J.** about one-third of the way down the sticks

5. Which of these steps comes after making the frame?
    ○ **A.** making the bridle
    ○ **B.** making the tail
    ● **C.** covering the kite
    ○ **D.** flying the kite

Name _____

Information and Study Skills *(comparing information in different forms)*

Read passages A and B. Then read each question and fill in the circle next to the best answer.

Passage **A** is part of George Washington's journal, which he wrote at age sixteen. The entry tells about a trip young George took with George William Fairfax, a family friend. Notice that some expressions are different from those used today.

A

A Journal of my Journey over the Mountains began Friday the 11th of March 1747.

Tuesday 15th. We set out early, . . . worked hard until night, and then returned to Penningtons . . . we got our suppers and were lighted into a room and I . . . went into the bed, as they called it, when to my surprise I found it to be nothing but a little straw matted together without sheets or anything else but only one . . . blanket with double its weight of . . . lice fleas. . . . Had we not have been very tired, I am sure we should not have slept much that night. I made a promise not to sleep so from that time forward choosing rather to sleep in the open air before a fire. . . .

Passage **B** tells about George Washington's childhood. The passage is from the web site of George Washington's home, Mount Vernon.

B

When George was eleven years old, his father died. George became very close to his older half-brother, Lawrence. . . . George enjoyed listening to Lawrence talk about . . . the Virginia frontier. One day, George learned that Lawrence's friend, George William Fairfax, was going to the frontier to survey land. George wanted to go. He had learned a little about surveying and had practiced by measuring Lawrence's turnip field. Although he was only sixteen years old, Mr. Fairfax allowed him to join the group. . . . The men rode on horseback for days exploring the wilderness. They slept in the open, still wearing their clothes and rolled up in blankets. . . .
George wrote about these experiences in his journal.

Go on ▷

1. What makes passage **A** a primary source?

   ● **A.** It was written about a period in history by a person who lived during that time.

   ○ **B.** It is a journal entry written from the narrator's point of view.

   ○ **C.** It tells about a person who was important in the history of our country.

   ○ **D.** It is written in language that is old-fashioned and difficult to understand.

2. What is the purpose of passage **A**?

   ○ **F.** to describe George William Fairfax

   ○ **G.** to explain why it is better to sleep outside

   ● **H.** to record George Washington's thoughts while on a journey

   ○ **J.** to persuade the reader to write in a journal

3. What is the most important thing readers can get from reading passage **A**?

   ○ **A.** knowledge about George William Fairfax

   ○ **B.** information about the Potomac River

   ● **C.** a sense of what life was like in an earlier time

   ○ **D.** an explanation of why George Washington slept outside

4. What makes passage **B** a secondary source?

   ○ **F.** It gives one person's opinion about how a famous person lived.

   ○ **G.** It is a narrative that tells about a famous person's life.

   ● **H.** It is written about an era by someone who was not a firsthand witness.

   ○ **J.** It gives a detailed description of people and events from an earlier time.

5. What is the purpose of passage **B**?

   ○ **A.** to inform readers about how long George Washington was away from home

   ● **B.** to inform readers about George Washington's childhood

   ○ **C.** to describe the close relationship between George Washington and his brother Lawrence

   ○ **D.** to persuade the reader to study the life and family of George Washington

STOP

Possessives and Contractions

Choose the word or words that mean about the same as the underlined part of each sentence. Fill in the circle next to the best answer.

1. <u>We'll</u> visit the scene of the Boston Tea Party.
   - ○ **A.** We would
   - ○ **B.** We could
   - ● **C.** We will
   - ○ **D.** We still

2. The guide said, "Next, <u>you're</u> going aboard that ship."
   - ○ **F.** your
   - ● **G.** you are
   - ○ **H.** you sure
   - ○ **J.** you our

3. The <u>colonists'</u> costumes included feathers.
   - ○ **A.** colonist is
   - ○ **B.** colonist has
   - ○ **C.** colonist does
   - ● **D.** belonging to the colonists

4. The British <u>soldier's</u> uniform was red.
   - ● **F.** belonging to the soldier
   - ○ **G.** soldier has
   - ○ **H.** soldier does
   - ○ **J.** soldier is

5. The <u>patriot's</u> about to begin his speech.
   - ○ **A.** patriot has
   - ● **B.** patriot is
   - ○ **C.** belonging to the patriot
   - ○ **D.** patriot was

Name _____

Syllabication: VCCV and VCV Patterns

Choose the correct way to divide into syllables the underlined word in each sentence. Fill in the circle next to the best answer.

1. The man sprinkled <u>powder</u> on his wig.
    - ○ **A.** powde • r
    - ○ **B.** po • wder
    - ● **C.** pow • der
    - ○ **D.** powd • er

2. The <u>lunar</u> eclipse lasted a long time.
    - ● **F.** lu • nar
    - ○ **G.** lun • ar
    - ○ **H.** luna • r
    - ○ **J.** l • unar

3. She gave a <u>gentle</u> laugh.
    - ○ **A.** ge • ntle
    - ● **B.** gen • tle
    - ○ **C.** gent • le
    - ○ **D.** g • entle

4. The dog <u>behaved</u> well during the party.
    - ○ **F.** beha • ved
    - ○ **G.** behav • ed
    - ○ **H.** beh • aved
    - ● **J.** be • haved

5. I heard the colonist <u>whisper</u> a warning.
    - ● **A.** whis • per
    - ○ **B.** whisp • er
    - ○ **C.** wh • isper
    - ○ **D.** whi • sper

Name _____

Prefixes *sub-* and *sur-*

Choose the correct meaning for each underlined word. Fill in the circle next to the best answer.

1. Brad's <u>subcompact</u> car fit easily into the parking space.
   - ● **A.** smaller than a compact
   - ○ **B.** larger than a truck
   - ○ **C.** equal in size to a compact
   - ○ **D.** smaller than a van

2. He went into the <u>substation</u> to mail the letter.
   - ○ **F.** original station
   - ○ **G.** main station
   - ○ **H.** large station
   - ● **J.** smaller station

3. Please <u>survey</u> the flood damage and then report to the mayor.
   - ○ **A.** look under
   - ● **B.** look over
   - ○ **C.** look ahead
   - ○ **D.** look toward

4. The <u>submarine</u> craft traveled slowly around the island.
   - ○ **F.** above the water
   - ○ **G.** near the water
   - ● **H.** under the water
   - ○ **J.** through the water

5. The problems with the design were too great to <u>surmount</u>.
   - ○ **A.** learn
   - ○ **B.** know about
   - ○ **C.** add to
   - ● **D.** overcome

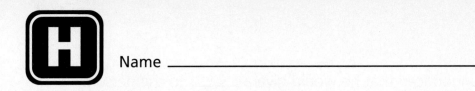

Name _____

Spelling *(final /ər/; final /l/ or /əl/)*

Find the correctly spelled word to complete each sentence. Fill in the circle beside your answer.

1. The daughter of the _____ of Lexington was married.
   - ○ **A.** mayer
   - ○ **B.** mayir
   - ● **C.** mayor
   - ○ **D.** mayier

2. The wedding was held in the lower _____ of the family's home.
   - ○ **F.** levol
   - ● **G.** level
   - ○ **H.** levil
   - ○ **J.** leval

3. The guests gathered in the _____.
   - ● **A.** parlor
   - ○ **B.** parlur
   - ○ **C.** parlar
   - ○ **D.** parler

4. The bride glanced over her _____ at her mother.
   - ○ **F.** shouldar
   - ○ **G.** shouldur
   - ● **H.** shoulder
   - ○ **J.** shouldor

5. The bride looked as lovely as the _____ in her ring.
   - ○ **A.** jewol
   - ○ **B.** jewil
   - ○ **C.** jewal
   - ● **D.** jewel

Go on ▷

6. The bride's father announced that he would give a _____ to the person who guessed the name of his dog.
   - ○ **F.** quartor
   - ○ **G.** quartir
   - ○ **H.** quartier
   - ● **J.** quarter

7. He gave a _____ and the dog came running.
   - ○ **A.** whislte
   - ● **B.** whistle
   - ○ **C.** whistal
   - ○ **D.** whistel

8. Not one _____ person guessed the dog's name.
   - ○ **F.** singel
   - ○ **G.** singal
   - ● **H.** single
   - ○ **J.** singol

9. The dog was named _____ because it was always happy.
   - ○ **A.** Sparkal
   - ● **B.** Sparkle
   - ○ **C.** Sparkul
   - ○ **D.** Sparkol

10. The guests enjoyed the man's sense of _____.
   - ● **F.** humor
   - ○ **G.** humer
   - ○ **H.** humar
   - ○ **J.** humur

Name _____

Vocabulary

Read each sentence. Then answer the question about the underlined word. Fill in the circle next to the best answer. *(synonyms, antonyms)*

1. *The old trunk was cherished by the family.*

    Which word means the **same** as *cherished*?

    ○ **A.** opened   ○ **C.** stored

    ○ **B.** moved   ● **D.** loved

2. *Mrs. Harrison kept cloth in the trunk.*

    Which word means the **same** as *cloth*?

    ○ **F.** clothes   ○ **H.** books

    ● **G.** fabric   ○ **J.** odds and ends

3. *Like the furnishings in the house, the trunk was plain.*

    Which word means the **same** as *plain*?

    ● **A.** simple   ○ **C.** fancy

    ○ **B.** heavy   ○ **D.** broken

4. *The soldiers pushed past the woman into the house.*

    Which word means the **same** as *pushed*?

    ○ **F.** rolled   ○ **H.** strolled

    ○ **G.** skipped   ● **J.** shoved

5. *They were quite noisy as they searched the house.*

    Which word means the **opposite** of *noisy*?

    ○ **A.** chatty   ○ **C.** slow

    ● **B.** silent   ○ **D.** awkward

6. *I felt upset to have soldiers in my home.*

Which word means the **opposite** of *upset*?

○ **F.** worried   ● **H.** calm

○ **G.** excited   ○ **J.** bored

7. *When they left, the house was very messy.*

Which word means the **opposite** of *messy*?

● **A.** neat   ○ **C.** untidy

○ **B.** cluttered   ○ **D.** small

Use the chart to answer the questions. Fill in the circle next to the best answer. *(spelling table, pronunciation key)*

Sound	Spellings	Sample Words
/yōō/	u_e, u, ew, ue	cube, music, few, cue
/ŭ/	u, o, o_e, ou, oe, oo, u_e	duck, son, some, double, does, blood, judge

8. Which of these could be a sample word for the sound /ŭ/?

○ **F.** hoop   ○ **H.** road

○ **G.** pond   ● **J.** skunk

9. Which of these could be a sample word for the sound /yōō/?

○ **A.** large   ○ **C.** ramp

● **B.** fume   ○ **D.** skit

10. Which of these letter pairs can stand for both the /yōō/ sound and the /ŭ/ sound?

○ **F.** ou   ○ **H.** ue

○ **G.** oe   ● **J.** u_e

Name _____

Grammar *(subject-verb agreement; regular and irregular verbs; adjectives; proper adjectives; verb phrases with have; teach, learn; let, leave; sit, set; can, may)*

Choose the sentence that is written correctly. Fill in the circle next to the best answer.

1. ○ **A.** The colonists wants freedom. *(subject-verb agreement)*
   ○ **B.** King George refuse to grant them certain rights.
   ● **C.** He places a tax on tea.
   ○ **D.** I knows that this is not fair.

2. ● **F.** Sara picks up the shovel. *(subject-verb agreement)*
   ○ **G.** She dig ditches between the rows of plants.
   ○ **H.** She are happy to see several small seedlings already.
   ○ **J.** Her neighbors gathers to help her with the garden.

3. ● **A.** Paul gave the message to the farmers. *(regular and irregular verbs)*
   ○ **B.** Who gived Paul such a message?
   ○ **C.** John gaved it to him yesterday.
   ○ **D.** All the farmers have gaven the message to their friends.

4. ○ **F.** The patriot runned away from the soldiers. *(regular and irregular*
   ○ **G.** The patriot had ran into the secret meeting. *verbs)*
   ○ **H.** The soldiers had ranned after him.
   ● **J.** He has run from the soldiers several times.

5. ○ **A.** Benjamin Franklin walks down an alleys of Philadelphia. *(adjectives)*
   ● **B.** He walks in front of a carriage.
   ○ **C.** The man such as this needs to be careful.
   ○ **D.** He has a important job to do.

6. ○ **F.** Take care of these paper for John Adams. *(adjectives)*
   ○ **G.** Put them in this folder across the room.
   ● **H.** Then read this book about the colonies.
   ○ **J.** Please do this jobs before you leave.

7. ○ **A.** The english settlers faced many hardships. *(proper adjectives)*
   ○ **B.** During the french and Indian War, they needed help.
   ● **C.** The British king was afraid of losing the colonies.
   ○ **D.** He sent supplies and soldiers to the american continent.

8. ○ **F.** The colonists has practiced firing their muskets. *(verb phrases with*
   ● **G.** They have loaded the carts with supplies.   *have)*
   ○ **H.** Their leader have asked two people to ride ahead.
   ○ **J.** I has hoped I could go.

                                                   (teach, learn; let, leave; sit, set; can, may)
9. ○ **A.** Tom Able's mother does not leave him fight in the army.
   ○ **B.** Instead, she learn him how to take care of the farm.
   ● **C.** He set a sack of feed in the barn.
   ○ **D.** Then he set on a stool to milk the cow.

                                                   (teach, learn; let, leave; sit, set; can, may)
10. ○ **F.** "Can I go to the Town Hall meeting?" asked Abigail.
    ○ **G.** "I cannot leave you go until later," said Mr. Brown.
    ○ **H.** "I need you to set by Ana's bed until she wakes," he explained.
    ● **J.** "May she come with me?" asked Abigail excitedly.

Name _____

Writing Skills *(using exact nouns and verbs)*

**Replace each underlined noun or verb with a more exact word.
Fill in the circle next to your answer.**

1. Abigail Adams placed a vase of white <u>flowers</u> on her desk.
   - ● **A.** roses
   - ○ **B.** plants
   - ○ **C.** stems
   - ○ **D.** leaves

2. A sea gull <u>flew</u> high over the ships in Boston's harbor.
   - ○ **F.** went
   - ○ **G.** moved
   - ○ **H.** dropped
   - ● **J.** soared

3. The colonist <u>held</u> the secret document tightly to his chest.
   - ○ **A.** pulled
   - ● **B.** clutched
   - ○ **C.** tipped
   - ○ **D.** pushed

**Find the sentence that is correct. Fill in the circle next to your
answer.** *(capitalizing names of people and places)*

4. ○ **F.** John Hancock was the first person to sign the Declaration of
   Independence in philadelphia, Pennsylvania.
   ● **G.** John Hancock was the first person to sign the Declaration of
   Independence in Philadelphia, Pennsylvania.
   ○ **H.** John hancock was the first person to sign the Declaration of
   Independence in Philadelphia, pennsylvania.
   ○ **J.** John hancock was the first person to sign the Declaration of
   Independence in philadelphia, Pennsylvania.

5. ○ **A.** Soldiers from new Hampshire arrived to help Colonel William prescott.
   ○ **B.** Soldiers from New Hampshire arrived to help Colonel william Prescott.
   ● **C.** Soldiers from New Hampshire arrived to help Colonel William Prescott.
   ○ **D.** Soldiers from new hampshire arrived to help Colonel
   William Prescott.

STOP

Person to Person

Level 5, Theme 4

Theme Skills Test Record

Student _____ Date _____

Student Record Form	Possible Score	Criterion Score	Student Score
Part A: Problem Solving and Decision Making	5	4	
Part B: Noting Details	5	4	
Part C: Compare and Contrast	5	4	
Part D: Making Inferences	5	4	
Part E: Information and Study Skills	5	4	
Part F: Syllabication: VCCCV Pattern	5	4	
Part G: Syllabication: VV Pattern	5	4	
Part H: Words Ending in *-ed* or *-ing*	5	4	
Part I: Suffixes *-ly, -ness, -ment, -ful, -less*	5	4	
Part J: Spelling	10	8	
Part K: Vocabulary	10	8	
Part L: Grammar	10	8	
Part M: Writing Skills	5	4	
TOTAL	80	64	
Total Student Score x 1.25 =			%

Problem Solving and Decision Making

Read the passage. Then read each question and fill in the circle next to the best answer.

The Best Solution

It was the day of the city parks' basketball championship. We were all gathered at the court when Sara, our best free-throw shooter, sat down on a bench and said, "I don't feel very well, Coach."

"What's wrong?"

"My stomach . . . my head . . . I think I'm coming down with the flu."

"It's just nerves," said Alvin, our center. "You'll be fine, Sara."

Coach looked at Sara and shook his head. "No, you definitely look pale," he said.

"Take deep breaths, Sara," said Linda, our small forward. "And say to yourself 'I won't be sick, I won't be sick. . . .'"

Coach shook his head. "Forget it. Sara has to go straight to bed. The only thing we can do is forfeit the game."

"*Forfeit?*" Everyone groaned. "But we've worked so hard!"

"Hey, what about my brother, Casey?" I said. "He shoots free throws from his wheelchair better than I can on two good legs."

"But . . . he's never played with us before," said Linda.

"I've seen him play," said Sara. "He's awesome."

"It might be against the rules," said Wally.

"Does anyone have a better idea?" asked Coach.

Alvin shrugged. "We can't forfeit, that's for sure."

Coach turned to me with a grin. "Doug, go get your brother," he said. "Win or lose, we're fielding a team today."

1. What was the problem faced by the team?
   - ○ **A.** Casey was in a wheelchair.
   - ● **B.** The team's best free-throw shooter was sick.
   - ○ **C.** The coach was sick.
   - ○ **D.** They had to forfeit the game.

2. Which of these solutions was **not** suggested?
   - ○ **F.** Have Casey play instead of Sara.
   - ○ **G.** Have Sara take deep breaths.
   - ○ **H.** Forfeit the game.
   - ● **J.** Have Coach play instead of Sara.

3. What solution was chosen?
   - ○ **A.** Forfeit the game.
   - ● **B.** Ask Casey to fill in.
   - ○ **C.** Have Sara take deep breaths.
   - ○ **D.** Have Sara take some aspirin.

4. Why was the chosen solution the best one?
   - ○ **F.** It was Coach's idea.
   - ○ **G.** It wasn't against the rules.
   - ● **H.** Casey was a good basketball player.
   - ○ **J.** The best athletes always play through pain.

5. Why weren't the other players' solutions chosen?
   - ○ **A.** They weren't fair to Casey.
   - ● **B.** They weren't fair to Sara.
   - ○ **C.** They hurt Coach's feelings.
   - ○ **D.** They were against the rules.

Name _____

Noting Details

Read the passage. Then read each question and fill in the circle next to the best answer.

Helping Leila Achieve Her Dream

At the age of three, Leila Josefowicz began taking music lessons. Even though she was very young, she loved to listen to her parents' recordings of classical music. As she listened, she sometimes made up stories to go with the music. She decided at a young age that she wanted to learn to play the violin very well.

Today, Leila is a well-known violinist. She has performed with orchestras from Amsterdam to Dallas. Her love of the music helped her achieve her goal. Yet she could not have achieved her dream without the help of many people.

When Leila was growing up, she practiced the violin about four hours every day. She awakened at six o'clock every morning to practice before school. Then she practiced more before she did her homework after school. She even practiced after dinner. Her father would often stay near her as she worked. This helped her feel his support. He also drove her to Los Angeles twice a week.

In Los Angeles, Leila worked with her teacher, Robert Lipsett. If Leila had difficulty with part of a piece, Mr. Lipsett would help her by showing her how to play it. He was patient with her, and he helped her have a good time at her lessons by making her laugh.

Leila's brother and mother helped her, too. Sometimes Steven, her brother, played tether ball with her. At other times, she would take long walks along the beach at Malibu with her brother, her mother, and the dog, Molly. The walks helped Leila to stay relaxed. They also gave the family members time to joke around and have fun.

Many people admire Leila's talent. She would be the first to say, however, that a person's talent depends on a lot of love and support from others.

Go on ⟹

1. Which detail helps you know that Leila wanted to become a musician even when she was very young?

   ○ **A.** Her father stayed near her while she practiced playing the violin.
   ○ **B.** She took lessons in Los Angeles from Mr. Robert Lipsett.
   ○ **C.** She took long walks on the beach with her mother and brother.
   ● **D.** She decided that she wanted to learn to play the violin really well.

2. What detail tells you that Leila is a successful violinist?

   ○ **F.** Leila walked on the beach at Malibu.
   ○ **G.** Leila's brother played tether ball with her.
   ● **H.** Leila has played in orchestras around the world.
   ○ **J.** Leila loved listening to classical music at age three.

3. Based on the passage, which of these adults did **not** help Leila achieve her dream?

   ○ **A.** Leila's father
   ○ **B.** Mr. Robert Lipsett
   ● **C.** Leila's uncle
   ○ **D.** Leila's mother

4. Which word tells you that Robert Lipsett made learning fun?

   ● **F.** laugh
   ○ **G.** patient
   ○ **H.** difficulty
   ○ **J.** time

5. Which detail tells you that Leila was committed to her music?

   ○ **A.** She had a dog named Molly.
   ● **B.** She practiced about four hours a day.
   ○ **C.** Her teacher lived in Los Angeles.
   ○ **D.** Her father supported her.

Name _____

Compare and Contrast

Read the passage. Then read each question and fill in the circle next to the best answer.

Elena's Two Homes

My name is Elena Fuentes. For most of the year, I live with my mother in San Antonio, Texas. During the summers, we live in Monterrey, Mexico, with my grandmother. I moved to Texas from Monterrey only two years ago, so I feel that Mexico is my real home. In San Antonio, I live in a small apartment. In Mexico, my grandmother's house is very big. My favorite room there is the huge kitchen. I can look at the beautiful view of the mountains from the kitchen window and smell the fragrant dishes that are always cooking on the large stove.

Like my grandmother, my mother loves to cook. However, she works all day when we are in San Antonio. At the end of the day, we usually prepare something quick and easy in our tiny kitchen. On the weekends, we sometimes make flan, a rich custard. My grandmother and I both prefer flan to any other dish.

I think that the hardest part of living in a new country is learning to speak the language. Luckily, my teacher and friends help me learn new words every day. Luckily, too, I have a few close friends in San Antonio. Since we live in different neighborhoods, we ride the bus to school. I do miss my friends in Mexico very much, though. There, I had many friends, and we walked to school together every day.

When I'm in San Antonio, I also miss having pets to play with. I love to play with the pets at my grandmother's house. I throw sticks for Pedrito, her dog, and stroke Gato's soft fur. Gato is a yellow cat that loves to lick the flan from my fingers. We're not allowed to keep pets in our apartment. My mother says that when we move to a house, I can have a kitten. I can't wait!

1. How is Elena's kitchen in San Antonio different from her grandmother's kitchen?
   - ○ **A.** It is filled with wonderful smells.
   - ○ **B.** It has a large stove.
   - ○ **C.** It has a view of the mountains.
   - ● **D.** It is very small.

2. How are Elena and her grandmother alike?
   - ● **F.** They both love flan.
   - ○ **G.** They both speak English well.
   - ○ **H.** They both live in San Antonio for part of the year.
   - ○ **J.** They both live in Monterrey all year.

3. How do Elena's friendships in Mexico differ from her friendships in San Antonio?
   - ○ **A.** She has fewer friends in San Antonio, and they walk to school with her.
   - ○ **B.** She had more friends in Mexico, and they lived in different neighborhoods.
   - ○ **C.** She had fewer friends in Mexico, and they all lived on the same street.
   - ● **D.** She had more friends in Mexico, and they walked to school with her.

4. How are Elena's grandmother and mother alike?
   - ○ **F.** They both visit Monterrey every summer.
   - ● **G.** They both love to cook.
   - ○ **H.** They both like to walk to school with Elena.
   - ○ **J.** They both have a dog and a cat.

5. Which of these is a reason that Elena likes being in Mexico better than being in San Antonio?
   - ○ **A.** In San Antonio, she lives in a large house.
   - ○ **B.** In Mexico, she can fix quick and easy meals.
   - ● **C.** In Mexico, she can play with her grandmother's pets.
   - ○ **D.** In San Antonio, she has a view of the mountains.

STOP

Name _____

Making Inferences

Read the passage. Then read each question and fill in the circle next to the best answer.

The Reason Why

"How about a snack?" Kim asked Alicia. Alicia, a new girl at school, had come home with Kim. Earlier that week Alicia had told Kim how difficult it was to be a new student at a school. Kim wanted to make Alicia feel welcome. She even hoped that she and Alicia would become close friends.

A few minutes later, Kim's older brother walked into the kitchen carrying a tennis racket. "Hi, I'm Lee," he said. Alicia's face lit up when she saw Lee. Soon the two were talking excitedly about tennis while Kim fixed sandwiches. As they ate, Alicia and Lee continued talking. It seemed to Kim that Alicia had completely forgotten about her.

When they finished eating, Kim suggested that she and Alicia go outside to play with Petunia, the family's dog. Lee followed, suggesting that they throw tennis balls to Petunia.

Later, after Alicia had gone home, Kim began to pout. She said, "Thanks a lot, Lee. I think you and Alicia were both rude. Now, whenever she comes over, she'll be coming to see you, not me."

Lee was surprised at his sister's outburst. They rarely had disagreements. He didn't even know what he had done wrong. He thought he had simply been a good host to Kim's friend.

Although Kim's feelings were still hurt, she greeted Alicia with a smile the next day at school. Alicia told Kim that she had enjoyed her visit. "I'm so glad that I got to meet Lee," she said. "I have a brother his age." Then her face fell. "I don't get to see him very often, though. He goes to college in another state. It's so lonely without him."

Kim immediately understood that Alicia had not been rude at all. "We loved having you visit us," she replied. "Why don't you call your mother and ask her if you can come again today?"

Go on ▷

1. How do you know that Alicia's family has probably moved recently?
   - ○ **A.** She talks about moving to a new house.
   - ● **B.** She tells Kim how difficult it is to be a new girl in school.
   - ○ **C.** She says she has not yet finished unpacking.
   - ○ **D.** She talks about how her brother moved away.

2. Why does Alicia's face light up when she sees Lee?
   - ○ **F.** Lee is in one of Alicia's classes.
   - ○ **G.** Alicia has another friend named Lee.
   - ● **H.** Lee reminds Alicia of her brother.
   - ○ **J.** Lee reminds Alicia of her best friend.

3. Which of these does Alicia most likely do as a hobby?
   - ● **A.** She plays tennis.
   - ○ **B.** She makes different kinds of snacks.
   - ○ **C.** She runs track.
   - ○ **D.** She takes a course at the local college.

4. Why does Kim pout when Alicia leaves?
   - ● **F.** She is angry that Lee talked to Alicia so much.
   - ○ **G.** She worries that Alicia didn't like her dog.
   - ○ **H.** She doesn't want to talk about tennis.
   - ○ **J.** Lee didn't help her fix the snack.

5. How does Kim most likely feel at the end of the story?
   - ○ **A.** She is angry at Lee and Alicia.
   - ● **B.** She feels relieved to know why Alicia talked to Lee.
   - ○ **C.** She resents that Alicia has a brother, too.
   - ○ **D.** She is excited that Lee will be at home that afternoon.

Information and Study Skills *(note taking; paraphrasing and synthesizing)*

Read paragraphs A and B. Then answer the questions that follow. Fill in the circle next to the best answer.

A student writing a paper on Alexander Graham Bell found the following information. She found Paragraph A in a book called *Famous Inventors*. She found Paragraph B in a newspaper article.

A. Alexander Graham Bell was born in 1847 in Edinburgh, Scotland. As an adult, he moved to Boston, Massachusetts. <u>Bell worked to help people who could not hear well. This interest led him to invent the telephone in 1876.</u> News of his invention quickly spread throughout the country. Bell set up the first telephone exchange in New Haven, Connecticut. By 1884, long distance connections had been established between Boston, Massachusetts, and New York City.

B. If Alexander Graham Bell were alive today, he would be amazed at how his invention has changed the world. Today, people who have trouble hearing use special telephones to communicate with their friends. People around the world use telephone lines to send instant e-mail messages to one another. The same telephone lines allow people to use the Internet to study, shop, and find information about a wide variety of subjects. Telephone lines allow people to communicate with one another in ways that Alexander Graham Bell would never have dreamed of.

1. Which of these is a paraphrase of the underlined sentences in Paragraph A?
   - ○ **A.** Bell worked to help people who could not hear well; this interest led him to invent the telephone in 1876.
   - ● **B.** Bell's invention of the telephone in 1876 resulted from his work with people who could not hear well.
   - ○ **C.** Bell helped people who could not hear well.
   - ○ **D.** Bell invented the telephone in 1876.

2. Which of these sentences paraphrases the last sentence in Paragraph A?
   - ○ **F.** Long distance connections were set up.
   - ○ **G.** Alexander Graham Bell established connections between Boston and New York City in 1884.
   - ● **H.** Long distance connections between Boston and New York City were made by 1884.
   - ○ **J.** By 1876, long distance connections had been made between Boston and New York.

3. Which of these sentences synthesizes the ideas in both paragraphs?
   - ○ **A.** The first long distance connections ever made occurred between Boston and New York City.
   - ○ **B.** Alexander Graham Bell changed the course of history.
   - ○ **C.** Today, people who have trouble hearing can use special telephones.
   - ● **D.** Bell's invention of the telephone in 1876 led to today's developments in communications.

4. What would be the best heading for a note card with the following note: *born in 1847 in Edinburgh, Scotland*?
   - ○ **F.** Notes for My Report
   - ○ **G.** Famous Inventors
   - ● **H.** Bell's Early Life
   - ○ **J.** Quotations for My Report

5. What important detail would you record under the heading *Telephone Lines Today*?
   - ○ **A.** the year the telephone was invented
   - ● **B.** how the Internet uses telephone lines
   - ○ **C.** the location of the first telephone exchange
   - ○ **D.** how Alexander Graham Bell invented the first telephone

STOP

Name _____

Syllabication: VCCCV Pattern

Choose the correct way to divide into syllables the underlined word in each sentence. Fill in the circle next to the best answer.

1. He is <u>extracting</u> the nail from the board.
   - ○ **A.** extr • act • ing
   - ● **C.** ex • tract • ing
   - ○ **B.** extra • ct • ing
   - ○ **D.** ext • ract • ing

2. The teacher was quite <u>impressed</u> with the student's skill.
   - ● **F.** im • pressed
   - ○ **H.** impre • ssed
   - ○ **G.** imp • ressed
   - ○ **J.** impr • essed

3. Amy signed a <u>contract</u> when she began working for the company.
   - ○ **A.** cont • ract
   - ○ **C.** contr • act
   - ● **B.** con • tract
   - ○ **D.** co • ntract

4. He was flattered by the <u>compliment</u>.
   - ○ **F.** compl • im • ent
   - ○ **H.** co • mpli • ment
   - ○ **G.** comp • li • ment
   - ● **J.** com • pli • ment

5. Let's not <u>exclude</u> anyone from the game.
   - ● **A.** ex • clude
   - ○ **C.** exclu • de
   - ○ **B.** excl • ude
   - ○ **D.** exc • lude

STOP

Name _____

Syllabication: VV Pattern

Choose the correct way to divide into syllables the underlined word in each sentence. Fill in the circle next to the best answer.

1. The <u>audience</u> clapped politely at the end of the concert.
   - ○ **A.** aud • ie • nce
   - ○ **B.** au • dien • ce
   - ○ **C.** aud • ien • ce
   - ● **D.** au • di • ence

2. The pilot knew a lot about <u>aviation</u>.
   - ○ **F.** av • ia • tion
   - ● **G.** a • vi • a • tion
   - ○ **H.** avia • ti • on
   - ○ **J.** a • via • tion

3. Marty doesn't like to watch movies that have <u>violent</u> scenes.
   - ○ **A.** vio • lent
   - ● **B.** vi • o • lent
   - ○ **C.** v • io • lent
   - ○ **D.** viol • ent

4. The <u>librarian</u> helped me with my science report.
   - ○ **F.** li • bra • rian
   - ○ **G.** lib • ra • r • ian
   - ○ **H.** li • bra • ria • n
   - ● **J.** li • brar • i • an

5. He conducted a <u>scientific</u> study of alligators.
   - ● **A.** sci • en • tif • ic
   - ○ **B.** scie • nt • if • ic
   - ○ **C.** scien • ti • fic
   - ○ **D.** sc • ien • ti • fic

Name _____

Words Ending in *-ed* or *-ing*

Read each sentence. Then fill in the circle next to the word that best completes each sentence.

1. Jana was _____ about her birthday gift.
   - ● **A.** bragging
   - ○ **B.** brags
   - ○ **C.** bragged
   - ○ **D.** brag

2. Lily had _____ a large glass of orange juice.
   - ○ **F.** orders
   - ○ **G.** order
   - ● **H.** ordered
   - ○ **J.** ordering

3. Jamal doesn't find clowns very _____.
   - ○ **A.** amuse
   - ● **B.** amusing
   - ○ **C.** amuses
   - ○ **D.** amused

4. They _____ special invitations last night.
   - ○ **F.** decorating
   - ● **G.** decorated
   - ○ **H.** decorates
   - ○ **J.** decorate

5. Yesterday, she _____ to help him with his science homework.
   - ● **A.** offered
   - ○ **B.** offer
   - ○ **C.** offering
   - ○ **D.** offers

STOP

Name _____

Suffixes *-ly, -ness, -ment, -ful, -less*

Choose the correct meaning for each underlined word. Fill in the circle next to the best answer.

1. My best friend <u>eagerly</u> accepted her award for helping young children.
   - ● **A.** in an eager way
   - ○ **B.** lacking eagerness
   - ○ **C.** wanting to be eager
   - ○ **D.** able to be eager

2. The <u>happiness</u> she felt showed on her face.
   - ○ **F.** wanting to be happy
   - ○ **G.** not being happy
   - ○ **H.** having the power to be happy
   - ● **J.** the condition of being happy

3. In her <u>excitement</u>, she did not see the edge of the stage.
   - ○ **A.** able to be excited
   - ○ **B.** not being excited
   - ● **C.** the condition of being excited
   - ○ **D.** wanting to be excited

4. I was <u>fearful</u> that she might fall down.
   - ○ **F.** without fear
   - ● **G.** full of fear
   - ○ **H.** able to have fear
   - ○ **J.** using fear

5. The boy was <u>speechless</u> after he received his award.
   - ● **A.** without speech
   - ○ **B.** full of speech
   - ○ **C.** using speech
   - ○ **D.** able to have speech

Spelling

Find the correctly spelled word to complete each sentence. Fill in the circle beside your answer.

1. My father and I like to go to the _____ each year. *(vv pattern)*

- ○ **A.** roadio
- ● **B.** rodeo
- ○ **C.** rodio
- ○ **D.** roadeo

2. This year we _____ to buy cowboy hats to wear. *(words with -ed or -ing)*

- ○ **F.** decyded
- ● **G.** decided
- ○ **H.** diecided
- ○ **J.** deacided

3. We each made a _____ to take in case we got hungry. *(vcccv pattern)*

- ○ **A.** sanwich
- ○ **B.** sanwhich
- ○ **C.** sandwitch
- ● **D.** sandwich

4. My father also packed a _____ so he could listen to the news. *(vv pattern)*

- ● **F.** radio
- ○ **G.** raydio
- ○ **H.** reidio
- ○ **J.** radeo

5. This year we had to walk _____ than ever from the parking lot. *(vcccv pattern)*

- ○ **A.** father
- ● **B.** farther
- ○ **C.** farthur
- ○ **D.** farthir

Go on ⟩

6. I tried not to _____ even though walking made me tired. *(vcccv pattern)*

- ● **F.** complain
- ○ **G.** complayn
- ○ **H.** complane
- ○ **J.** complaine

7. We _____ to watch the bull riding event first. *(words with -ed or -ing)*

- ○ **A.** planed
- ○ **B.** plaaned
- ● **C.** planned
- ○ **D.** plannd

8. The clowns kept a _____ eye on the angry bulls. *(words with suffixes -ly, -ness, -ment, -ful, -less)*

- ○ **F.** watchfull
- ○ **G.** wachful
- ● **H.** watchful
- ○ **J.** washful

9. Their _____ tricks kept people laughing. *(words with -ed or -ing)*

- ○ **A.** amuzing
- ● **B.** amusing
- ○ **C.** amewsing
- ○ **D.** ahmusing

10. They _____ waved flags at the bull when the riders fell. *(words with suffixes -ly, -ness, -ment, -ful, -less)*

- ○ **F.** activly
- ○ **G.** activley
- ● **H.** actively
- ○ **J.** acktively

Name _____

Vocabulary

Read each sentence. Fill in the circle next to the best answer.

1. Under which entry word would you look in the dictionary to find the
    meaning of *laughed*? *(dictionary: base words and inflected forms)*
    ○ **A.** laughed   ○ **C.** laughter
    ○ **B.** laughing   ● **D.** laugh

2. Under which entry word would you look in the dictionary to find the
    meaning of *hiding*? *(dictionary: base words and inflected forms)*
    ○ **F.** hid   ○ **H.** hiding
    ● **G.** hide   ○ **J.** hidden

3. Under which entry word would you look in the dictionary to find the
    meaning of *convincing*? *(dictionary: base words and inflected forms)*
    ● **A.** convince   ○ **C.** convinced
    ○ **B.** convinc   ○ **D.** convincing

4. Complete the sentence with the word that has a positive connotation.
    (connotation)
    A _____ breeze blew through the town.
    ○ **F.** frigid   ○ **H.** wintry
    ● **G.** cool   ○ **J.** chilly

5. Complete the sentence with the word that has a negative connotation.
    (connotation)
    We worked all day under the _____ sun.
    ○ **A.** bright   ○ **C.** shining
    ○ **B.** glowing   ● **D.** scorching

Go on ⇨

Read the following sentences. Find the definition for the underlined word. Fill in the circle next to the best answer.
(multiple-meaning words)

6. It is a <u>rule</u> of the soccer club that anyone may play.

   ○ **F.** to govern
   ○ **G.** an order by a court of law
   ○ **H.** to mark with lines
   ● **J.** a statement of what to do

7. After her third <u>foul</u>, the basketball player was taken out of the game.

   ○ **A.** dirty
   ○ **B.** tangled up
   ● **C.** an unfair play
   ○ **D.** rainy or stormy

Read the dictionary entries in the chart. Find the definition for the underlined word. Fill in the circle next to the best answer.
(dictionary: prefixes)

in-	A prefix that means "not."
com-	A prefix that means "together" or "with."
re-	A prefix that means "again" or "back."

8. His answer to the math question was <u>incorrect</u>.

   ● **F.** not right
   ○ **G.** better
   ○ **H.** almost right
   ○ **J.** a good effort

9. The machine <u>compressed</u> the sheets of cardboard into small stacks.

   ○ **A.** pushed away
   ○ **B.** found a difference
   ○ **C.** separated into two parts
   ● **D.** squeezed together

10. Before I knew it, my friend <u>reappeared</u> in the doorway.

   ○ **F.** leaned against
   ○ **G.** stood
   ● **H.** came into view again
   ○ **J.** walked through

Name _____

Grammar

Choose the sentence that is written correctly. Fill in the circle next to the best answer.

1. ○ **A.** Patty please bring me the scissors, tape, and chalk. *(commas in a*
   ○ **B.** Patty, please bring me the scissors, tape and chalk. *series; commas with*
   ● **C.** Patty, please bring me the scissors, tape, and chalk. *direct address)*
   ○ **D.** Patty please bring me the scissors tape, and chalk.

2. ○ **F.** W. E. Riley felt goodest than he had ever felt before. *(comparing with*
   ○ **G.** W E. Riley felt gooder than he had ever felt before. *good and bad;*
   ● **H.** W. E. Riley felt better than he had ever felt before. *abbreviations)*
   ○ **J.** W E. Riley felt best than he had ever felt before.

3. ● **A.** Oops, I didn't know that Jason is taller than Ann. *(comparing with*
   ○ **B.** Oops I didn't know that Jason is tall than Ann. *adjectives; inter-*
   ○ **C.** Oops, I didn't know that Jason is tallest than Ann. *jections)*
   ○ **D.** Oops I didn't know that Jason is taller than Ann.

(commas used with **yes**; *titles)*

4. ○ **F.** Yes I have read the poem "Listen to Your Friends" three times.
   ○ **G.** Yes, I have read the poem Listen to Your Friends three times.
   ○ **H.** Yes, I have read the poem Listen To Your Friends three times.
   ● **J.** Yes, I have read the poem "Listen to Your Friends" three times.

(commas in a series; quotations)

5. ○ **A.** "I'm supposed to take cups napkins, and plates to the class picnic," said Maria.
   ● **B.** "I'm supposed to take cups, napkins, and plates to the class picnic," said Maria.
   ○ **C.** "I'm supposed to take cups, napkins, and plates to the class picnic" said Maria.
   ○ **D.** "I'm supposed to take cups, napkins and plates to the class picnic, said Maria.

Go on ⟫

6. ○ **F.** Wow! I'm the taller person in the class. *(comparing with adjectives;*
   ○ **G.** Wow I'm the tallest person in the class. *interjections)*
   ○ **H.** Wow I'm the tall person in the class.
   ● **J.** Wow! I'm the tallest person in the class.

(abbreviations; quotations)

7. ○ **A.** The teacher said "My name is Ms. Alice N. Hawes."
   ○ **B.** The teacher said, My name is Ms. Alice N. Hawes.
   ● **C.** The teacher said, "My name is Ms. Alice N. Hawes."
   ○ **D.** The teacher said, "My name is Ms Alice N. Hawes."

8. ○ **F.** The worstest book I've ever read is New Times. *(comparing with*
   ● **G.** New Times is the worst book I've ever read. *good or bad; titles)*
   ○ **H.** New Times is the worser book I've ever read.
   ○ **J.** "New Times" is the worst book I've ever read.

9. ● **A.** Abby said, "Let's take the softball, mitt, and bat." *(commas in a*
   ○ **B.** Abby said. "Let's take the softball, mitt, and bat." *series; quotations)*
   ○ **C.** Abby said, "Let's take the softball, mitt and bat."
   ○ **D.** Abby said, "Let's take the softball, mitt, and bat.

(comparing with adjectives; titles)

10. ○ **F.** "Let's Go" is a shorter book than "The Beach in Winter."
   ● **G.** Let's Go is a shorter book than The Beach in Winter.
   ○ **H.** Let's Go is a shortest book than The Beach In Winter.
   ○ **J.** Let's Go is a shorter book than The Beach In Winter.

M Name _____

Writing Skills *(combining sentences by using introductory phrases)*

Read the passage. Then read each question and fill in the circle next to the best answer.

¹The family began to prepare for their trip to the beach. ²It was early in the morning. ³Dad made potato salad and sandwiches. ⁴He was in the kitchen.

⁵Mom found the ice chest. ⁶It was in the garage. ⁷Gloria packed the beach towels. ⁸She was in the den.

⁹Gloria put the swim suits in the trunk. ¹⁰She did this right before they left.

1. Which of these shows the best way to combine sentences 1 and 2?
   - **A.** Early in the morning, the family began to prepare for their trip to the beach.
   - ○ **B.** The family began to prepare, early in the morning, for their trip to the beach.
   - ○ **C.** The family began to prepare for their trip to the beach, early in the morning.
   - ○ **D.** Early the family began to prepare for their trip to the beach in the morning.

2. Which of these shows the best way to combine sentences 3 and 4?
   - ○ **F.** Dad made potato salad and sandwiches, and he was in the kitchen.
   - ○ **G.** Dad made potato salad and sandwiches, when he was in the kitchen.
   - ○ **H.** Dad made potato salad in the kitchen and sandwiches in the kitchen.
   - **J.** In the kitchen, Dad made potato salad and sandwiches.

3. Which of these shows the best way to combine sentences 5 and 6?

   ○ **A.** Mom found in the garage the ice chest.

   ○ **B.** Mom in the garage found the ice chest.

   ● **C.** Mom found the ice chest in the garage.

   ○ **D.** Mom found the ice chest, and it was in the garage.

4. Which of these shows the best way to combine sentences 7 and 8?

   ● **F.** In the den, Gloria packed the beach towels.

   ○ **G.** Gloria packed the beach towels, and she was in the den.

   ○ **H.** Gloria packed, in the den, the beach towels.

   ○ **J.** Gloria in the den packed the beach towels.

5. Which of these shows the best way to combine sentences 9 and 10?

   ○ **A.** Gloria put the swim suits, right before they left, in the trunk.

   ● **B.** Right before they left, Gloria put the swim suits in the trunk.

   ○ **C.** Gloria put, right before they left, the swim suits in the trunk.

   ○ **D.** They left right before Gloria put the swim suits in the trunk.

One Land, Many Trails

Level 5, Theme 5

Theme Skills Test Record

Student _____ Date _____

Student Record Form

	Possible Score	Criterion Score	Student Score
Part A: Drawing Conclusions	5	4	
Part B: Propaganda	5	4	
Part C: Making Judgments	5	4	
Part D: Story Structure	5	4	
Part E: Information and Study Skills	5	4	
Part F: Prefixes *un-*, *dis-*, *in-*, *re-*; Suffix *-ion*	5	4	
Part G: Stressed and Unstressed Syllables	5	4	
Part H: Syllabication	5	4	
Part I: Changing Final *y* to *i*	5	4	
Part J: Spelling	10	8	
Part K: Vocabulary	10	8	
Part L: Grammar	10	8	
Part M: Writing Skills	5	4	
TOTAL	80	64	
Total Student Score x 1.25 =			%

Drawing Conclusions

Read the passage. Then read each question and fill in the circle next to the best answer.

The Pony Express

The Pony Express marked one of the most exciting times in the history of the West. Three men formed the business in 1860. They wanted to show the government that they could deliver mail between Missouri and California. They hoped that the government would eventually hire them and their new business would make a lot of money.

The men planned for a relay of riders to carry the mail between the states. They set up stations every ten to fifteen miles where the riders could change horses. The stations formed a 2000-mile trail. Next, the owners hired riders to carry the mail. To do this, they posted the following ad:

"Wanted. Young, skinny, wiry fellows. Not over 18. Must be expert riders. Willing to risk death daily."

Riders who signed on with the Pony Express had a very tough job. They galloped at full speed from station to station. At each station, they leapt from one horse, mounted another, and raced ahead. When a rider had traveled about seventy-five to one hundred miles, he handed the mail off to a new rider, who continued the journey.

The difficult trip took about ten days in the summer and twelve to sixteen days in the winter. The shortest trip was the delivery of a copy of the speech that Abraham Lincoln gave when he became President. It took only seven days and seventeen hours.

When the Pony Express began, customers paid five dollars to have a letter delivered. Later, however, the price dropped to one dollar. The Pony Express ended in 1861 when the telegraph, which allowed people to send messages by telegram, was invented. Even though the Pony Express did not last very long, its brave, young riders will always be remembered.

1. Why did the owners of the Pony Express set up a relay rather than sending one man at a time?
   - ● **A.** The relay made the delivery of the mail faster.
   - ○ **B.** The relay made the delivery of the mail more exciting for the riders.
   - ○ **C.** Riders didn't want to face the dangers of the trip alone.
   - ○ **D.** Riders wanted to see other people as they worked.

2. Why did each rider ride more than one horse?
   - ○ **F.** All the horses needed to be exercised.
   - ○ **G.** There were different horses waiting at each station.
   - ○ **H.** Riding more than one horse made the trip more interesting.
   - ● **J.** The horses became tired after running so hard.

3. How many relay stations were set up?
   - ○ **A.** a few
   - ○ **B.** a dozen
   - ○ **C.** a half-dozen
   - ● **D.** many

4. Why did the trip take longer in winter?
   - ○ **F.** The riders followed a different trail.
   - ○ **G.** The riders spent a long time at each station.
   - ● **H.** Bad weather made traveling more difficult.
   - ○ **J.** The horses couldn't run as fast in the winter.

5. Why did the Pony Express end the same year that the telegraph was invented?
   - ○ **A.** Many horses were sick that year.
   - ● **B.** The telegraph allowed people to send messages more quickly than the Pony Express.
   - ○ **C.** All the Pony Express riders went to work for the telegraph companies.
   - ○ **D.** The owners of the Pony Express sold their business to the telegraph companies.

STOP

B

Name _____

Propaganda

Read the passage. Then read each question and fill in the circle next to the best answer.

Cowboys Needed

Rusty McCall needs cowhands to help him round up and break wild mustangs. If you need some money, this may be the job for you.

"The job is exciting and just plain fun. There's nothing more thrilling than climbing on the back of an untamed mustang," says McCall, known all around the West for his riding skills.

If you want to apply, you must be an expert roper and rider. You must also have experience rounding up horses. All the cowboys who helped during the last roundup had the best time of their lives. They received some of the highest pay in the area.

You will be paid one whole dollar a day. In addition, each cowboy will receive three hot, delicious meals every day. Comfortable housing will be provided in the bunkhouses at the ranch. The bunkhouses hold sixteen men each.

Don't miss out! Cowboys from far and wide will soon be trying to rope this once-in-a-lifetime opportunity. Sign up now so you won't be left in the dust.

1. What is the purpose of this passage?
    - ○ **A.** to describe the life of a cowboy
    - ● **B.** to encourage cowboys to work for Rusty McCall
    - ○ **C.** to evaluate the life of a cowboy
    - ○ **D.** to express an opinion about wild mustangs

2. Which statement is an example of overgeneralization?

○ **F.** Rusty McCall needs cowhands to help him round up and break wild mustangs.

○ **G.** If you want to apply, you must be an expert roper and rider.

● **H.** All the cowboys who helped during the last roundup had the best time of their lives.

○ **J.** The pay is one whole dollar a day.

3. What form of propaganda is used in the following statement?

"There's nothing more thrilling than climbing on the back of an untamed mustang," says McCall, known around the state for his riding skills.

● **A.** testimonial

○ **B.** bandwagon

○ **C.** transfer

○ **D.** faulty cause and effect

4. What form of propaganda is used in the last paragraph of the passage?

● **F.** bandwagon

○ **G.** overgeneralization

○ **H.** testimonial

○ **J.** transfer

5. Which of the following statements about the job is most likely to be true?

○ **A.** The bunk beds are comfortable.

○ **B.** The meals are all delicious.

○ **C.** The cowboys will have fun.

● **D.** The bunkhouses hold sixteen men each.

Making Judgments

Read the journal entry. Then read each question and fill in the circle next to the best answer.

May 9, 1856

Journal Entry written by Clyde Snider

The school I go to is a small frame house with only one room. It has a blackboard and five rows of desks. During recess, we play in a nearby field or under the big oak tree in the schoolyard. I really enjoy walking to school every day.

My teacher's name is Miss Tucker. She's kind and patient, and I've learned a lot from her. In the winter, she arrives early to start a fire in the wood-burning stove. At noon, she cooks a meal for us while we play outside.

Miss Tucker brings books, maps, and supplies to school whenever she can find them. She makes difficult lessons easy to understand, and she gives us lots of practice exercises to help us learn. I enjoy all my subjects, although mathematics is sometimes hard for me.

The students range from first grade through eighth grade. Even though everyone has to study something different, Miss Tucker makes lessons for everyone. Sometimes the older students help the younger ones.

Unfortunately, I have a problem at school, and his name is Jamie Livermore. Jamie used to be a good friend of mine, and he's the best marble player in the county. Lately, though, he's been a bother. Whenever I need to work in class, he starts talking to me. He keeps talking until I turn around and ask him to be quiet. Then we both get into trouble. Yesterday, we had to stand in front of the class for fifteen minutes as punishment. Last week, we had to chop wood after school. I don't mind chopping wood, but I don't like being punished because Jamie doesn't follow the rules.

Tomorrow we're going to write a play about the explorers. Miss Tucker wants me to help two of the younger students. Tomorrow night, I'll write in my journal about what happens.

Go on ⟹

1. Which fact supports the judgment that Miss Tucker is a good teacher?
   ○ A. She makes Jamie and Clyde chop wood.
   ● B. She is good at explaining things.
   ○ C. She builds fires in the winter.
   ○ D. She is kind and patient.

2. Which fact supports the judgment that Clyde is a good student?
   ○ F. He likes to walk to school.
   ○ G. He likes his teacher.
   ○ H. He and Jamie used to be good friends.
   ● J. He helps out the younger students.

3. Which of these judgments could be based on the fact that Jamie talks in class?
   ● A. Jamie gets his friend in trouble.
   ○ B. Jamie is not a good student, especially in math.
   ○ C. Jamie is one of the best marble players in the county.
   ○ D. Jamie is a popular student.

4. From the information in the journal, what judgment can you make about Clyde's school?
   ● F. The school was very different from today's schools.
   ○ G. The students in Clyde's school learned more than today's students do.
   ○ H. Miss Tucker was always well prepared.
   ○ J. Going to school then was more fun than it is today.

5. From the information in the journal, which judgment can you make about one-room schoolteachers in the 1800s?
   ○ A. The teachers had to like to walk.
   ○ B. The teachers had an easy job.
   ● C. The teachers had to work very hard.
   ○ D. The teachers did not need to know much.

Name _____

Story Structure

Read the passage. Then read each question and fill in the circle next to the best answer.

The Trip to Town

Sally and her sister Amanda sat in the back of the wagon as it bumped along the road. "I can't wait to get to the general store," Sally said. "Ma said we could buy fabric to make new dresses. What color will you choose?"

Just as Amanda opened her mouth to answer, the wagon jerked to a stop. The horses tossed their heads, unable to pull the wagon any farther.

Pa climbed down and looked at the back left wheel. "It's stuck," he explained. "Everybody climb down and help me unload these sacks of grain. Unless we work quickly, we won't have time to go to the general store."

The family began lifting a dozen sacks of grain from the wagon. Pa needed to sell the grain at the market in town. While they worked, Sally hoped she didn't have to wait for next week's trip to get the fabric for her new dress.

When the wagon was finally empty, Pa helped Ma into the driver's seat. Ma picked up the reins. Then Pa slowly lifted the back of the wagon while Ma snapped the reins gently. The wagon lurched, then rolled easily forward. They reloaded the grain and soon they were on their way again.

At midmorning, they reached the edge of town. Sally saw people strolling along the wooden sidewalks. "Is there time to go to the general store, Pa?" she asked. Then she held her breath.

Pa reached into his pocket and pulled out a watch. He smiled as he answered, "I suppose we can spare a few minutes." Soon Sally was standing in front of racks of brightly colored fabrics. She immediately saw the green fabric she wanted. Before she knew it she was back in the wagon, rolling and bumping toward home.

1. Who is the main character in this story?
   - ○ **A.** Pa
   - ○ **B.** Ma
   - ○ **C.** Amanda
   - ● **D.** Sally

2. Where does most of the story take place?
   - ○ **F.** at the family home
   - ○ **G.** in the general store
   - ● **H.** on the road to town
   - ○ **J.** at the market

3. What is the problem in the story?
   - ○ **A.** Pa has to sell a dozen sacks of grain.
   - ● **B.** The wagon gets stuck.
   - ○ **C.** The horses toss their heads nervously.
   - ○ **D.** There is not enough fabric for two dresses.

4. What is one of the steps that helps to solve the problem?
   - ○ **F.** Pa takes a watch out of his pocket.
   - ○ **G.** Amanda opens her mouth to speak.
   - ○ **H.** Sally chooses a green fabric.
   - ● **J.** The family unloads the grain.

5. What is the most important reason that the family needs to get to town?
   - ● **A.** Pa needs to sell the sacks of grain.
   - ○ **B.** They need to get the wagon wheel fixed.
   - ○ **C.** The girls need to buy fabric.
   - ○ **D.** Pa needs to get a new watch.

Information and Study Skills *(comparing information from more than one source)*

Read paragraphs A, B, C, and D. Then answer the questions that follow. Fill in the circle next to the best answer.

A. From the diary of Annie Stanley, 1850

The early days were the worst. My husband left for work before dawn and mined for gold all day. One day, I decided to open a hotel. I started by serving hot meals to miners at a cost of a dollar a meal. Soon, I had saved enough money to build a hotel with five guest rooms. . . .

B. From *Encyclopedia of the West*

Because he needed lumber for his ranch, James Sutter sent about twenty men to the American River to build a sawmill in late 1847. James Marshall was one of these men. In January, 1848, at the river, Marshall found a lump of gold the size of a small pea. Soon after, he found another and another. Men with him began to find gold, too. Word of Marshall's discovery spread quickly. By the end of 1848, people along the east coast had heard the news. . . .

C. From *California Times* newspaper, June 7, 2001

Gold Fever: The Story of the 49ers, an exciting exhibition, will open today at the Museum of History. Visitors to the exhibition will view tools used by the miners, paintings showing events that occurred during the period, and photographs of actual events. . . .

D. From *The Real Story About the 49ers*, by Rupert McDonald, director of the *Gold Rush Association*

In my opinion, although the 49ers changed history, they ruined one of the most beautiful regions in our country. . . .

1. Which source provides an eyewitness account?
   - ● **A.** A
   - ○ **B.** B
   - ○ **C.** C
   - ○ **D.** D

2. Which sources would be most likely to contain biased information?
   - ○ **F.** A and B
   - ○ **G.** B and C
   - ○ **H.** C and D
   - ● **J.** A and D

3. Which source would be most likely to provide objective details about the daily life of many people during the Gold Rush?
   - ○ **A.** A
   - ○ **B.** B
   - ● **C.** C
   - ○ **D.** D

4. Which source would be most likely to have accurate information about dates of important events during the Gold Rush?
   - ○ **F.** A
   - ● **G.** B
   - ○ **H.** C
   - ○ **J.** D

5. What is the author's purpose for writing paragraph **A?**
   - ● **A.** to describe her experiences
   - ○ **B.** to explain how to mine for gold
   - ○ **C.** to state her opinion about the Gold Rush
   - ○ **D.** to help people learn more about the Gold Rush

Prefixes *un-*, *dis-*, *in-*, *re-*; Suffix *-ion*

Choose the correct meaning for each underlined word. Fill in the circle next to the best answer.

1. Charles was <u>unprepared</u> for the test.
   - ● **A.** not prepared
   - ○ **B.** well prepared
   - ○ **C.** badly prepared
   - ○ **D.** prepared before

2. Becky <u>disagreed</u> with his decision.
   - ○ **F.** agreed before
   - ● **G.** did not agree
   - ○ **H.** partly agreed
   - ○ **J.** mostly agreed

3. The colts were <u>inactive</u> in the cold.
   - ○ **A.** very active
   - ○ **B.** able to be active
   - ○ **C.** more than active
   - ● **D.** not active

4. The ranch hands <u>rebuilt</u> the corral.
   - ○ **F.** built before
   - ○ **G.** did not build
   - ● **H.** built again
   - ○ **J.** took apart

5. The <u>reflection</u> of the rising sun shone in the lake.
   - ○ **A.** something that is not reflected
   - ● **B.** something that is reflected
   - ○ **C.** badly reflected
   - ○ **D.** to reflect

Name _____

Stressed and Unstressed Syllables

**Choose the word in which the syllables are stressed correctly.
Fill in the circle next to the best answer.**

1. She can trace her <u>ancestors</u> back to Greece.

   ○ **A.** an CES tors
   ○ **B.** an ces TORS
   ○ **C.** AN ces TORS
   ● **D.** AN ces tors

2. The little boy could <u>multiply</u> the numbers in his head.

   ● **F.** MUL ti ply
   ○ **G.** mul TI ply
   ○ **H.** mul TI PLY
   ○ **J.** MUL TI ply

3. <u>Agriculture</u> was their only way to make a living.

   ○ **A.** ag RI cul ture
   ● **B.** AG ri cul ture
   ○ **C.** ag ri cul TURE
   ○ **D.** ag ri CUL ture

4. They packed all of their <u>belongings</u> into the covered wagon.

   ○ **F.** be long INGS
   ○ **G.** BE long ings
   ○ **H.** BE LONG ings
   ● **J.** be LONG ings

5. A high <u>percentage</u> of people would not survive the cold winter.

   ○ **A.** PER CENT age
   ○ **B.** per cent AGE
   ● **C.** per CENT age
   ○ **D.** PER cent age

STOP

Syllabication *(vv, vcv, vccv, vcccv patterns)*

Choose the correct way to divide into syllables the underlined word in each sentence. Fill in the circle next to the best answer.

1. The cook <u>created</u> many dishes for the ranchers.
    - ○ **A.** cr • eat • ed
    - ○ **B.** crea • te • d
    - ○ **C.** cr • ea • ted
    - ● **D.** cre • at • ed

2. The ground was <u>solid</u> after years of dry weather.
    - ○ **F.** so • lid
    - ● **G.** sol • id
    - ○ **H.** s • olid
    - ○ **J.** soli • d

3. The hard <u>surface</u> made plowing difficult.
    - ○ **A.** su • rface
    - ● **B.** sur • face
    - ○ **C.** surfa • ce
    - ○ **D.** surf • ace

4. In an <u>instant</u> the clouds opened and rain fell.
    - ○ **F.** ins • tant
    - ○ **G.** inst • ant
    - ○ **H.** insta • nt
    - ● **J.** in • stant

5. The rancher held an <u>empty</u> bucket.
    - ● **A.** emp • ty
    - ○ **B.** empt • y
    - ○ **C.** em • pty
    - ○ **D.** e • mpty

Name _____

Changing Final *y* to *i*

Choose the correct base word for each underlined word below.
Fill in the circle next to the best answer.

1. Ricardo <u>steadied</u> his horse as he rode toward the herd.
    - ● **A.** steady
    - ○ **B.** steadi
    - ○ **C.** study
    - ○ **D.** stead

2. He <u>carried</u> a rope in his hand to rope the missing steer.
    - ○ **F.** carri
    - ○ **G.** careful
    - ○ **H.** care
    - ● **J.** carry

3. The cowboy was <u>hungrier</u> than he had been in days.
    - ○ **A.** hungriest
    - ○ **B.** hungri
    - ● **C.** hungry
    - ○ **D.** hungeriest

4. The calves this spring are <u>healthier</u> than those born last year.
    - ○ **F.** healthi
    - ● **G.** healthy
    - ○ **H.** healthiest
    - ○ **J.** healthful

5. The cowboy wrote two <u>stories</u> about this adventure.
    - ○ **A.** storie
    - ○ **B.** store
    - ○ **C.** stores
    - ● **D.** story

STOP

Name _____

Spelling

Find the correctly spelled word to complete each sentence.
Fill in the circle beside your answer.

1. Mexican soldiers were seen riding in the _____. *(words with unstressed syllables)*
   - ○ **A.** distunce
   - ○ **B.** distaince
   - ○ **C.** distence
   - ● **D.** distance

2. Each one carried a _____ from his country. *(words with final /zhər/)*
   - ○ **F.** tresure
   - ● **G.** treasure
   - ○ **H.** treasur
   - ○ **J.** treazure

3. The mayor put up a _____ in the center of town. *(words with unstressed syllables/ final /ĭs/)*
   - ○ **A.** notis
   - ○ **B.** notise
   - ○ **C.** notic
   - ● **D.** notice

4. The mayor did not speak the same _____ as the soldiers. *(words with unstressed syllables/ final /ĭj/)*
   - ● **F.** language
   - ○ **G.** langwich
   - ○ **H.** languag
   - ○ **J.** langage

5. We polished the _____ in honor of the soldiers' arrival. *(words with final /chər/)*
   - ○ **A.** furnitur
   - ○ **B.** furnitare
   - ○ **C.** furnichur
   - ● **D.** furniture

Go on

6. The furniture had never been _____. *(changing final* y *to* i*)*

   ○ **F.** dirtior
   ● **H.** dirtier

   ○ **G.** dirtyer
   ○ **J.** dertier

7. The soldiers came riding down the _____ into town. *(words with final /n/)*

   ○ **A.** mountin
   ● **B.** mountain
   ○ **C.** muontain
   ○ **D.** mounten

8. Some people were _____ of their arrival. *(words with a prefix or a suffix)*

   ○ **F.** unawar
   ○ **G.** inaware
   ● **H.** unaware
   ○ **J.** unawhare

9. The _____ built as the soldiers rode through the streets. *(words with a prefix or a suffix)*

   ○ **A.** tenshun
   ● **B.** tension
   ○ **C.** tenchion
   ○ **D.** tinsion

10. My mother pushed aside the _____ to watch them ride by. *(words with final /ən/)*

   ○ **F.** curtin
   ○ **G.** curtan
   ● **H.** curtain
   ○ **J.** curtein

Vocabulary

Choose the word that best completes each analogy. Fill in the circle next to the best answer. *(analogies)*

1. Potato is to vegetable as piano is to _____.
   - ○ **A.** flute
   - ○ **B.** drum
   - ● **C.** instrument
   - ○ **D.** carrot

2. Plentiful is to rare as cramped is to _____.
   - ○ **F.** small
   - ● **G.** roomy
   - ○ **H.** many
   - ○ **J.** few

3. Lose is to misplace as locate is to _____.
   - ● **A.** find
   - ○ **B.** steal
   - ○ **C.** miss
   - ○ **D.** forget

Read these dictionary entries and answer the questions that follow. Fill in the circle next to the best answer. *(dictionary: suffixes)*

-less. A suffix that forms adjectives meaning "without, free of."

-ly. A suffix that forms adverbs and means "in a specified manner."

---

4. What is the meaning of the suffix in the underlined word?

   The stagecoach inched across the swiftly flowing river.
   - ● **F.** in a specified manner
   - ○ **G.** characteristic of
   - ○ **H.** without, free of
   - ○ **J.** full of

5. What is the meaning of the suffix in the underlined word?

   The ranchers' tireless efforts saved the herd.
   - ○ **A.** in a specified manner
   - ○ **B.** characteristic of
   - ● **C.** without, free of
   - ○ **D.** full of

Go on ▷

Read the following dictionary definition for the word *right*.
Then identify its part of speech in the sentences that follow.
Fill in the circle next to the best answer. *(dictionary: parts of speech)*

> **right** *n.* That which is morally proper or good. *-adj.* Located on the side opposite the left. *-adv.* In a correct manner, properly.

6. *Good role models teach kids the difference between right and wrong.*
   - ● **F.** noun
   - ○ **G.** verb
   - ○ **H.** adjective
   - ○ **J.** adverb

7. *He taught me that it's faster to do a job right the first time.*
   - ○ **A.** noun
   - ○ **B.** verb
   - ○ **C.** adjective
   - ● **D.** adverb

8. *If you have a question, please raise your right hand.*
   - ○ **F.** noun
   - ○ **G.** verb
   - ● **H.** adjective
   - ○ **J.** adverb

Read the following dictionary definitions. Then answer the questions that follow. Fill in the circle next to the best answer.
(dictionary: word histories)

> **mathematical** *adj.* Of or relating to mathematics. [From Greek *mathematikos*, from *mathema*, science, learning]
>
> **parade** *n.* An organized public procession. [From Latin *parare*, to prepare.]

9. On what word is the word *mathematical* based?
   - ○ **A.** the Latin word *parare*
   - ● **B.** the Greek word *mathematikos*
   - ○ **C.** the Greek word *parare*
   - ○ **D.** the Latin word *mathematikos*

10. What is the meaning of *parare*?
    - ○ **F.** science
    - ○ **G.** learning
    - ○ **H.** procession
    - ● **J.** prepare

STOP

Grammar

Choose the sentence that is written correctly. Fill in the circle next to the best answer. *(subject and object pronouns, possessive pronouns, double subjects, using I and me, contractions with pronouns, using we and us with nouns, adverbs, comparing with adverbs)*

1. ○ **A.** Mine father wants to find land in the West.
   ● **B.** His dream is to live in California.
   ○ **C.** He thinks that its a good time to move.
   ○ **D.** Im excited about having a new home.

2. ○ **F.** Jesse and Amber they like to ride horses.
   ○ **G.** Amber rides her horse fast than Jesse.
   ○ **H.** Amber says, "All the people at the stable know we girls."
   ● **J.** "We girls can ride any horse we want," says Jesse.

3. ● **A.** The girls rode swiftly through town.
   ○ **B.** One cowgirl whistled loud.
   ○ **C.** Final, they had found gold!
   ○ **D.** They sang songs and cheered happy.

4. ○ **F.** Hannah asked Sarah, Jim, and I to ride in her wagon.
   ○ **G.** "Could you give Bill and I a ride, too?" asked Sal.
   ● **H.** "Yes, you can come with me," replied Hannah.
   ○ **J.** Sarah and her hitched the horses to the wagon.

5. ● **A.** "Your farm is very pretty," said Mitzi.
   ○ **B.** "Mine neighbor helps us take care of it," replied Leah.
   ○ **C.** "Hes very good with the animals," said Leah.
   ○ **D.** "Us family members are happy for his help."

Go on ⇨

6. ○ **F.** "Ma, when are us going to stop for the night?" asked Amanda.
    ○ **G.** "Well stop at the river," said Ma.
    ○ **H.** "The wagon has been traveling smooth today," said Pa.
    ● **J.** "We've gone very far today, and I'm tired," said Austin.

7. ○ **A.** Pete and Graham they are learning how to herd cattle.
    ● **B.** They've been practicing by roping a post.
    ○ **C.** "Us boys will be as good as you soon," said Pete to Uncle Rick.
    ○ **D.** "Well, grab your saddles and lets go," said Uncle Rick.

8. ○ **F.** The horse runs more fast than the pony.
    ○ **G.** My horse runs the faster of all.
    ○ **H.** The winning horse must run more fastly than the others.
    ● **J.** The horse that runs fastest will win the race.

9. ● **A.** "Who is coming to see Luis and me?" asked Jorge.
    ○ **B.** "My mother and hers sister are coming to the ranch tonight," said Carmen.
    ○ **C.** "I'll watch for they," said Luis.
    ○ **D.** "Theyll be here before dark," said Carmen.

10. ○ **F.** Sandra likes hers teacher at the frontier school.
    ○ **G.** The teacher she is a woman who has taught for many years.
    ○ **H.** Shes in charge of students from first to twelfth grade.
    ● **J.** Hers is not an easy job.

Name _____

Writing Skills *(combining sentences with pronouns)*

Read the passage. Then read each question and fill in the circle next to the best answer.

Ma and Pa looked out over their land. They saw the new barn. They saw the crops growing in the fields.

A hen strutted across the yard. It clucked. It pecked at the ground. Then it flapped its wings.

A colt kicked up its heels in the pasture. It ran to the fence. It neighed at the dog. It ate a carrot from Ma's hand.

Pa picked up an ax. He began chopping wood. He began whistling a tune as he worked.

Ma worked in the garden. She planted tomatoes. She planted corn.

1. What is the best way to combine the sentences in the first paragraph?
   - ● **A.** Ma and Pa looked out over their land. They saw the new barn and the crops growing in the fields.
   - ○ **B.** After Ma and Pa looked out over their land, they saw the new barn. They saw crops growing in the fields.
   - ○ **C.** Ma and Pa looked out over their land. They saw crops growing in the fields, and they saw the new barn.
   - ○ **D.** Ma and Pa looked out over their land, and they saw crops and the new barn.

2. What is the best way to combine the sentences in the second paragraph?

   ○ **F.** A hen strutting across the yard clucked. It pecked at the ground. Then it flapped its wings.

   ○ **G.** A hen strutted across the yard. It clucked, it pecked at the ground, and it flapped its wings.

   ○ **H.** A hen strutted across the yard. It clucked, and it pecked at the ground. Then it flapped its wings.

   ● **J.** A hen strutted across the yard, clucked, pecked at the ground, and flapped its wings.

3. What is the best way to combine the sentences in the third paragraph?

   ○ **A.** A colt kicked up its heels, ran to the fence, it neighed at the dog, and ate a carrot.

   ○ **B.** A colt kicked up its heels in the pasture. It ran to the fence, and it neighed at the dog. Then it ate a carrot from Ma's hand.

   ● **C.** A colt kicked up its heels in the pasture, ran to the fence, neighed at the dog, and ate a carrot from Ma's hand.

   ○ **D.** A colt kicked up its heels in the pasture, and it ran to the fence. It neighed at the dog, and it ate a carrot from Ma's hand.

4. What is the best way to combine the sentences in the fourth paragraph?

   ● **F.** Pa picked up an ax and began chopping wood, whistling as he worked.

   ○ **G.** Pa picked up an ax, he began chopping wood, and he began whistling a tune as he worked.

   ○ **H.** Pa picked up an ax. He began chopping wood, and began whistling a tune as he worked.

   ○ **J.** Pa picked up an ax. He began chopping wood. He began whistling a tune as he worked.

5. What is the best way to combine the sentences in the fifth paragraph?

○ **A.** Ma worked in the garden. She planted tomatoes, she planted corn.

● **B.** Ma worked in the garden, planting tomatoes and corn.

○ **C.** Ma worked in the garden, and she planted tomatoes and she planted corn.

○ **D.** Ma worked in the garden. She planted tomatoes, and she planted corn.

Animal Encounters

Level 5, Theme 6

Theme Skills Test Record

Student _____ Date _____

Student Record Form		Possible Score	Criterion Score	Student Score
Part A:	Making Generalizations	5	4	
Part B:	Topic, Main Idea, and Supporting Details	5	4	
Part C:	Drawing Conclusions	5	4	
Part D:	Information and Study Skills	5	4	
Part E:	Prefixes *com-, con-, en-, ex-, pre-, pro-*	5	4	
Part F:	Three-Syllable Words	5	4	
Part G:	Suffixes *-ent, -ant; -able, -ible*	5	4	
Part H:	Spelling	10	8	
Part I:	Vocabulary	10	8	
Part J:	Grammar	10	8	
Part K:	Writing Skills	5	4	
TOTAL		70	56	
		Total Student Score x 1.43 =		%

Making Generalizations

Read the passage. Then read each question and fill in the circle next to the best answer.

Tonya's Kitten

Tonya's parents had promised her that she could get a dog or cat on her eleventh birthday. The day had come at last! She couldn't wait to go to the pet store in the mall. She knew that most pet owners love their pets, and she would, too.

Tonya's parents had told her that she would have to take care of the new pet by herself. She would give it water and food, and she would take care of it if it became ill.

Tonya's heart pounded in her chest as she walked into the pet store. She looked at the animals in their cages. The kittens were snuggled together, sound asleep. Like all puppies, the puppies were quite playful. Tonya didn't know which to choose, a puppy or a kitten.

Tonya asked the owner of the pet store for his advice. He said, "Owning a pet is always lots of fun. I think you should simply choose the animal that steals your heart."

Tonya walked past the cages again. A tiny brown puppy licked her hand. The puppy had soft fur and a pink tongue. Then Tonya walked over to the kittens. A black kitten awakened and stretched. The kitten looked at Tonya and meowed, as if to say, "Choose me!" It had the most beautiful green eyes Tonya had ever seen.

Tonya couldn't resist the kitten's plea. She picked it up and announced that the kitten would be her new pet. Then she asked the owner how to take care of it. He gave her several helpful hints and handed her a booklet called "Taking Care of Your Kitten."

When they got home, Tonya made a soft bed for her new kitten, Midnight. She held Midnight in her arms. "Cats make the best pets of all," she told her parents.

1. Which of the following sentences from the passage is an overgeneralization?
   - ○ **A.** She looked at the animals in their cages.
   - ○ **B.** Tonya asked the owner of the pet store for his advice.
   - ◉ **C.** Owning a pet is always lots of fun.
   - ○ **D.** Tonya walked past the cages again.

2. Based on the story, what generalization can you make about selecting a pet?
   - ◉ **F.** Selecting a pet can be very exciting.
   - ○ **G.** People usually select cats rather than dogs.
   - ○ **H.** Selecting a pet can take a very long time.
   - ○ **J.** People need help when selecting a pet.

3. Which word in the following sentence signals an overgeneralization?
   Like all puppies, the puppies were quite playful.
   - ○ **A.** like
   - ◉ **B.** all
   - ○ **C.** quite
   - ○ **D.** playful

4. Which of the following sentences from the story is a generalization?
   - ◉ **F.** Most pet owners love their pets.
   - ○ **G.** She couldn't wait to go to the pet shop at the mall.
   - ○ **H.** She would have to take care of the new pet by herself.
   - ○ **J.** The kittens were snuggled together, sound asleep.

5. Based on the story, what generalization can you make about taking care of a pet?
   - ○ **A.** Pets are very easy to care for.
   - ○ **B.** Pet owners always read books about their pets.
   - ○ **C.** Puppies are more playful than kittens.
   - ◉ **D.** Taking care of a pet is a big responsibility.

Topic, Main Idea, and Supporting Details

Read the passage. Then read each question and fill in the circle next to the best answer.

Please Don't Feed the Animals

Have you ever fed pieces of bread to a duck? Perhaps you have left picnic scraps for a squirrel. Even though it's fun to feed wild animals, it's almost always a bad idea. One reason for this is that the animals may become dependent on the food that people provide. The animals may also teach their young to beg for food. This may cause the animals to go too close to dangerous cars and homes. It's best if they stay in their natural habitats.

It's also dangerous for people to be around wild animals. Wild animals are interested in getting something to eat, not in making friends. If an animal learns that a certain person will give it food, the animal may chase that person. Geese often chase people with food. Squirrels have climbed up people's legs, scratching them. If a person receives such an injury from an animal, the person might become ill.

Another reason not to feed wild animals is that food that is good for people may not be healthy for animals. An animal's natural diet is well balanced for the animal. The food that people eat often contains more sugar, salt, and fat than animals need to be healthy. Some food may even kill an animal.

Feeding wild animals can also be expensive. The park rangers at national parks will charge a fine to a person who feeds wild animals. People who run the national forests want to keep the wildlife healthy. As a result, the fines may be as high as $500.00.

Go on ⟩

1. What is the topic of this passage?
   - ○ **A.** squirrels and geese
   - ○ **B.** diets of wild animals
   - ● **C.** feeding wild animals
   - ○ **D.** park rangers

2. Which sentence states the main idea of the passage?
   - ○ **F.** Some food that people eat can kill an animal.
   - ● **G.** People should not feed wild animals.
   - ○ **H.** Animals may chase people with food.
   - ○ **J.** It's best if animals stay in their natural habitats.

3. Which detail supports the idea that it's dangerous to be around wild animals?
   - ○ **A.** Animals may teach their young to beg for food.
   - ○ **B.** A person can be charged $500.00 for feeding a wild animal.
   - ○ **C.** An animal's natural diet is well balanced for the animal.
   - ● **D.** A person who is injured by an animal could become ill.

4. Which sentence from the third paragraph states the paragraph's main idea?
   - ● **F.** Another reason not to feed wild animals is that food that's good for people may not be healthy for animals.
   - ○ **G.** An animal's natural diet is well balanced for the animal.
   - ○ **H.** The food that people eat often contains more sugar, salt, and fat than animals need to be healthy.
   - ○ **J.** Some food may even kill an animal.

5. Which detail supports the main idea that feeding wild animals can be expensive?
   - ○ **A.** Animals may become dependent on the food that people feed them.
   - ○ **B.** Squirrels sometimes run up people's legs.
   - ○ **C.** Animals dependent on food from humans may come too close to cars.
   - ● **D.** Fines for feeding wild animals may be as high as $500.00.

STOP

Name _____

Drawing Conclusions

Read the passage. Then read each question and fill in the circle next to the best answer.

Erika's Gift

Erika tore the paper off her gift. "Just what I wanted!" she exclaimed. She held up a new camera and a roll of film.

Erika had decided that she wanted to become a wildlife photographer some day. She had spent hours looking at images of animals in magazines like *National Geographic*. She had read books about photography and cameras. Now she had her own camera! "A good place to start would be right in my own back yard," she thought.

Erika's house sat on the top of a hill. Her back yard sloped down to a clump of oak trees and a small pond. Her family often spotted raccoons, squirrels, birds, and even deer from the kitchen window. Erika liked to take walks in the yard just so she could be outside.

Erika carefully read the instruction booklet that came with the camera. Then she loaded the film. At last, she was ready to take some pictures! She went outside and walked toward the pond. Along the way, she took a picture of a blue jay. The blue jay flew away just as she snapped the shutter. This didn't discourage her, though, because she had read that photographers must take many pictures to get one good shot.

At that moment, Erika saw a deer walk to the pond. The deer didn't see her because she was several yards away. It looked cautiously around and then lowered its head. As it began drinking, Erika quietly adjusted the zoom lens on her camera. She knew that she could get a close-up shot of the deer even from this distance.

Erika aimed the camera at the deer and began clicking. When she had shot five pictures, she stopped. She wanted to have time to watch this beautiful animal before it wandered away. She smiled as she looked at the deer. She knew she had taken at least one fabulous shot.

1. Why does Erika feel that her own back yard is the best place to start taking pictures?

   ○ **A.** It is pretty.
   ○ **B.** She won't have to leave home.
   ○ **C.** It is safe.
   ● **D.** Her family sees animals there.

2. Which of the following details supports the conclusion that Erika knows a lot about photography?

   ○ **F.** She receives a camera and a roll of film as a gift.
   ● **G.** She reads many books and knows how to work the equipment.
   ○ **H.** She often spots wild animals from her kitchen window.
   ○ **J.** She takes a picture of a blue jay and several pictures of a deer.

3. Why does Erika know how to use a zoom lens?

   ● **A.** She read the instruction booklet.
   ○ **B.** She learned how to use it from her father.
   ○ **C.** She saw a show about it on television.
   ○ **D.** She learned about zoom lenses at school.

4. Which of these conclusions can you draw about Erika from reading the story?

   ○ **F.** She likes to roll down the hill in her yard.
   ● **G.** She likes being outdoors.
   ○ **H.** She often watches television shows about animals.
   ○ **J.** She is very close to her parents.

5. Why does Erika take five pictures of the deer?

   ○ **A.** She doesn't know how to work the camera.
   ○ **B.** The camera takes the pictures automatically.
   ● **C.** She wants to be sure to get one good shot.
   ○ **D.** She wants to have five good shots of the deer.

STOP

Name _____

Information and Study Skills
(completing applications and forms)

Read the application. Then answer the questions that follow. Fill in the circle next to the best answer.

Stephanie has signed up to help at the animal shelter in her town. Before she starts her job, she wants to learn as much as possible about animals. She goes to the library and picks up this application for a library card.

BOOKWORM LIBRARY CARD

To apply for a Bookworm Library Card, you must be under 16 years of age. Complete this form and turn it in to the main library or any branch. Bring an adult who has a photo I.D. and proof of address.

NAME

1. First Name _____ 2. Last Name _____

3. First and Last Name of Parent or Guardian _____

ADDRESS

4. Street _____ 5. Apartment No. ____

6. City _____ 7. State _____ 8. ZIP Code _____

PHONE NUMBER

9. Area Code/Phone Number _____

10. Phone Number of Parent or Guardian _____

IDENTIFICATION

11. Date of Birth Mo. Day. Yr. _____

12. Name of School _____

13. School's Phone Number _____

I understand that I should take good care of all library materials checked out in my name and that I should return them on time so others may enjoy them.

14. Signature _____

I assume responsibility for all materials checked out and all charges for materials that are turned in late. I understand that library fees are set by the city council and may change. I agree to inform the library if the card is lost or stolen.

15. Signature of Parent or Guardian _____ **Go on** ▷

---

1. What will Stephanie write on line 8?
   - ○ **A.** the name of her street
   - ● **B.** her ZIP code
   - ○ **C.** the name of her school
   - ○ **D.** her area code

2. What should Stephanie do if she doesn't know the phone number of her school?
   - ○ **F.** She should leave the line blank.
   - ○ **G.** She should call the school and ask.
   - ● **H.** She should look up the number in the phone book.
   - ○ **J.** She should write her home phone number.

3. Who should sign the form?
   - ○ **A.** only Stephanie
   - ○ **B.** Stephanie and the librarian
   - ● **C.** Stephanie and her parent or guardian
   - ○ **D.** only Stephanie's parent or guardian

4. What should Stephanie do with her completed application?
   - ○ **F.** use it to take out books at the library
   - ○ **G.** give it to her teacher
   - ○ **H.** turn it in at a city council meeting
   - ● **J.** take it to the main library or a branch library

5. What should Stephanie do **right after** she completes the application?
   - ● **A.** read it over to check for mistakes
   - ○ **B.** drop it in the mail
   - ○ **C.** take it to the library with a parent or guardian
   - ○ **D.** check out some books

Name _____

Prefixes *com-, con-, en-, ex-, pre-, pro-*

Choose the correct meaning for the underlined word or words in each sentence. Fill in the circle next to the best answer.

1. The camp director asked the group to <u>conform to</u> the rules.
   - ● **A.** agree with
   - ○ **B.** write
   - ○ **C.** read about
   - ○ **D.** break

2. Larry feeds his goldfish food that is <u>enriched</u> with iron.
   - ○ **F.** made of
   - ● **G.** made richer
   - ○ **H.** lacking in
   - ○ **J.** bitter

3. Colin <u>exchanged</u> five old books for a new book on African animals.
   - ○ **A.** bought for very little money
   - ○ **B.** gave away for free
   - ○ **C.** sold for a price
   - ● **D.** traded for a substitute

4. The hikers took a first-aid kit as a <u>precaution</u>.
   - ○ **F.** guidepost
   - ○ **G.** sign of danger
   - ● **H.** care taken in advance
   - ○ **J.** trail

5. The hikers <u>proceeded</u> to the spot where the bear had last been seen.
   - ○ **A.** walked away from
   - ● **B.** moved toward
   - ○ **C.** ran quickly
   - ○ **D.** hiked in pairs

STOP

Name _____

Three-Syllable Words

For each item, fill in the circle next to the word that is divided into syllables correctly.

1. *disagree*
   - ○ **A.** di • sag • ree
   - ○ **B.** dis • ag • ree
   - ● **C.** dis • a • gree
   - ○ **D.** di • sa • gree

2. *thankfully*
   - ○ **F.** than • kful • ly
   - ● **G.** thank • ful • ly
   - ○ **H.** thank • full • y
   - ○ **J.** tha • nkf • ully

3. *acceptance*
   - ● **A.** ac • cep • tance
   - ○ **B.** ac • cept • ance
   - ○ **C.** a • ccept • ance
   - ○ **D.** acc • ep • tance

4. *conference*
   - ● **F.** con • fer • ence
   - ○ **G.** conf • er • ence
   - ○ **H.** confe • re • nce
   - ○ **J.** con • fere • nce

5. *generous*
   - ○ **A.** ge • ner • ous
   - ○ **B.** gene • r • ous
   - ○ **C.** ge • nero • us
   - ● **D.** gen • er • ous

STOP

Suffixes *-ent, -ant; -able, -ible*

Choose the correct meaning for each underlined word. Fill in the circle next to the best answer.

1. Mrs. Smith was a new <u>resident</u> at my apartment building.
   - ○ **A.** window washer
   - ○ **B.** manager
   - ● **C.** neighbor
   - ○ **D.** gardener

2. The zookeeper is an <u>immigrant</u> from China.
   - ● **F.** someone who moves to a place
   - ○ **G.** a person who works with animals
   - ○ **H.** an important person
   - ○ **J.** someone who likes animals

3. The fragile glass swans were quite <u>breakable</u>.
   - ○ **A.** very sturdy
   - ● **B.** easily broken
   - ○ **C.** attractive
   - ○ **D.** very small

4. My mother says that Smokey the Bear hats and mugs are <u>collectibles</u>.
   - ○ **F.** books for collectors
   - ○ **G.** shelves to hold a collection
   - ○ **H.** a collector's displays
   - ● **J.** things that can be collected

5. The cowboy reported that the cattle herd was <u>manageable</u>.
   - ○ **A.** tired and hungry
   - ○ **B.** able to run very fast
   - ○ **C.** loud and rough
   - ● **D.** able to be controlled

H   Name _____

Spelling

Find the correctly spelled word to complete each sentence.
Fill in the circle beside your answer.

1. My class took a field trip to a wildlife _____. *(prefixes: pre-, pro-)*
   - ○ **A.** preserv
   - ○ **C.** proserve
   - ○ **B.** perserve
   - ● **D.** preserve

2. It was a beautiful day to walk in a _____ setting. *(three-syllable words)*
   - ○ **F.** naturl
   - ● **H.** natural
   - ○ **G.** natiral
   - ○ **J.** naturale

3. My teacher expressed his _____ about the environment. *(prefixes: con-, com-)*
   - ● **A.** concern
   - ○ **C.** comcern
   - ○ **B.** cuncern
   - ○ **D.** consern

4. He said that the lack of rain had created a _____ setting for the animals.
   (three-syllable words)
   - ○ **F.** dangrous
   - ○ **H.** dangerus
   - ● **G.** dangerous
   - ○ **J.** danjerous

5. He said that it was _____ that some of the animals would starve.
   (words with -able, -ible)
   - ● **A.** possible
   - ○ **C.** posible
   - ○ **B.** possibel
   - ○ **D.** possable

6. He told us that several species of animals were already _____ from the woods.
   (words with -ent, -ant)
   - ○ **F.** absant
   - ● **H.** absent
   - ○ **G.** abbsent
   - ○ **J.** abssent

Go on ⇨

7. At the park headquarters, we saw a _____ display.   *(words with -able, -ible)*

○ **A.** remarkible
● **B.** remarkable
○ **C.** remakable
○ **D.** remarckable

8. A woman explained that they must _____ certain rules for visitors.

○ **F.** enforse
○ **G.** inforse
○ **H.** inforce   *(prefix: en-)*
● **J.** enforce

9. She explained that the rules help maintain the good _____ of the park.

● **A.** condition
○ **B.** condishun
○ **C.** conditian   *(prefix: con-)*
○ **D.** cundition

10. I hope we can _____ more ideas about wildlife next week.   *(prefix: ex-)*

○ **F.** xchange
● **G.** exchange
○ **H.** exchang
○ **J.** exchainge

Name _____

Vocabulary

Choose the word or phrase that has the same meaning as the underlined word in each sentence. Fill in the circle next to the best answer.

1. The cheetah raced along at an amazing speed, easily <u>overtaking</u> the gazelle.
   (using context)
   ○ **A.** jumping higher than   ○ **C.** making friends with
   ○ **B.** falling behind   ● **D.** catching up with

2. Some male songbirds may <u>croon</u> a tune over 2000 times each day.
   (using context)
   ○ **F.** practice   ○ **H.** hear
   ● **G.** sing   ○ **J.** enjoy

3. A dog's hearing is so <u>acute</u> that it can hear sounds humans cannot.
   (using context)
   ○ **A.** attractive   ○ **C.** unaware
   ● **B.** sharp   ○ **D.** dull

4. The scientist carefully <u>excavated</u> the bones of the prehistoric creature from the hillside. *(using context)*
   ○ **F.** photographed   ● **H.** dug up
   ○ **G.** arranged   ○ **J.** fixed

Answer the following questions. Fill in the circle next to the best answer.

5. Under which entry word in the dictionary might you find the meaning of the underlined idiom? *(dictionary: idioms)*
   The finish was too close to call, so the results of the race are still <u>up in the air</u>.
   ○ **A.** in   ● **C.** air
   ○ **B.** the   ○ **D.** up

Go on ⟳

6. Under which entry word in the dictionary might you find the meaning of the underlined idiom? *(dictionary: idioms)*

The letter from my distant cousin Nate seemed to come out of the blue.

● **F.** blue   ○ **H.** of

○ **G.** out   ○ **J.** the

7. Under which word would you look in a dictionary to find the meaning of the word *tenderness*? *(dictionary: run-on entries)*

○ **A.** tend   ● **C.** tender

○ **B.** tending   ○ **D.** tenderly

8. Under which word would you look in a dictionary to find the meaning of the word *joyous*? *(dictionary: run-on entries)*

● **F.** joy   ○ **H.** joyfully

○ **G.** joyful   ○ **J.** joyless

Look at the following dictionary entry and use it to answer the questions. Fill in the circle next to the best answer.

---

falcon (**făl** kən) or (**fôl-**) or (**fô** kən) **n.** Any of several long-winged, swift-flying hawks.

---

9. How many different pronunciations are there for the word *falcon*?

○ **A.** one   ● **C.** three   *(dictionary: variations in pronunciation)*

○ **B.** two   ○ **D.** four

10. What two ways could the vowel sound in the first syllable of the word *falcon*?   *(dictionary: variations in pronunciation)*

○ **F.** like the vowel sound in *pay* or *pat*

● **G.** like the vowel sound in *pat* or *paw*

○ **H.** like the vowel sound in *pay* or *pot*

○ **J.** like the vowel sound in *paw* or *toe*

(STOP)

Name _____

Grammar

Choose the sentence that is written correctly. Fill in the circle next to the best answer.

1. ○ **A.** We cant find the monkeys. *(contractions with not)*
   ○ **B.** They have'nt been seen in several hours.
   ● **C.** They didn't come when we called.
   ○ **D.** We may'nt see them again.

2. ○ **F.** "Werent' you the one who wrote a paper on gorillas?" asked Gigi.
   ● **G.** "I didn't finish it," replied Alice. *(contractions with not)*
   ○ **H.** "I wont be able to help you with it," Gigi said.
   ○ **J.** "Tha'ts all right," said Alice.

3. ● **A.** They have no more food for the zebras at the zoo. *(negatives)*
   ○ **B.** I haven't ever seen no zebras at the zoo.
   ○ **C.** The zebras have not never been so friendly.
   ○ **D.** The giraffes can't not see them over the fence.

4. ○ **F.** The pet store sent a letter to she. *(object pronouns in*
   ○ **G.** My father read the letter to I. *prepositional phrases)*
   ○ **H.** The letter said that they would give we a gift.
   ● **J.** The gift will be delivered to her.

5. ○ **A.** My mother took a photograph of I with the cat. *(object pronouns in*
   ○ **B.** The children gathered around she to look at it. *prepositional phrases)*
   ○ **C.** My mother told they that the cat is named Little.
   ● **D.** She gave the picture to me after the picnic.

6. ○ **F.** Max threw the ball to Taylor and he.
   ○ **G.** Then Taylor threw it to Ellen and I.
   ● **H.** My dog brought the ball to Ernie and her.
   ○ **J.** We laughed at Mabel and she.

(object pronouns in prepositional phrases with compound objects)

Read the questions below. Fill in the circle next to the best answer.

7. What is the preposition in this sentence? *(prepositions)*

   Charles took the injured calf to the veterinarian.

   ○ **A.** took   ● **C.** to
   ○ **B.** the   ○ **D.** veterinarian

8. What is the preposition in this sentence? *(prepositions)*

   The man looked at the calf and sighed.

   ○ **F.** looked   ○ **H.** calf
   ● **G.** at   ○ **J.** sighed

9. What is the prepositional phrase in this sentence? *(prepositional phrases)*

   The calf put its head on the man's chest and blinked its eyes.

   ● **A.** on the man's chest   ○ **C.** put its head
   ○ **B.** The calf   ○ **D.** and blinked its eyes

10. What is the prepositional phrase in this sentence? *(prepositional phrases)*

    The man gently rubbed some medicine on the calf's leg.

    ○ **F.** The man   ○ **H.** some medicine
    ○ **G.** gently rubbed   ● **J.** on the calf's leg

Name _____

Writing Skills

Read the sentences below. Fill in the circle next to the sentence that is written correctly. *(avoiding double negatives)*

1. ○ **A.** The lion did not catch no prey today.
   ○ **B.** It never saw no other animals at all.
   ● **C.** The giraffes did not find very much food either.
   ○ **D.** They could never stretch their long necks high enough to get no leaves.

2. ○ **F.** Ana could not find no eggs in the chicken house.
   ● **G.** She looked under the bench but saw nothing there.
   ○ **H.** Jack didn't find no peaches in the peach trees.
   ○ **J.** He will not never plant that kind of tree again.

Choose the best way to combine each pair of sentences by using a prepositional phrase. Fill in the circle next to the best answer. *(combining sentences with prepositional phrases)*

3. Please get the puppy's leash. It is in the closet.
   ○ **A.** Please get the puppy's leash, because it is in the closet.
   ● **B.** Please get the puppy's leash from the closet.
   ○ **C.** Please get the puppy's leash which is in the closet.
   ○ **D.** Please get the puppy's leash; it is in the closet.

4. We saw a mother giraffe. She was with her baby.
   ● **F.** We saw a mother giraffe with her baby.
   ○ **G.** We saw a mother giraffe, and she was with her baby.
   ○ **H.** We saw a mother giraffe, and we saw her baby.
   ○ **J.** We saw a mother giraffe; she was with her baby.

5. The elephant is a large animal. It has huge floppy ears.
   ○ **A.** The elephant is a large animal, and it has huge floppy ears.
   ○ **B.** The elephant is a large animal; it has huge floppy ears.
   ○ **C.** The elephant is a large animal since it has huge floppy ears.
   ● **D.** The elephant is a large animal with huge floppy ears.